MW00647455

This is a continuation in the series of publications produced by the Center for Advanced Concepts and Technology (ACT), which was created as a "skunk works" with funding provided by the CCRP under the auspices of the Assistant Secretary of Defense (C3I). This program has demonstrated the importance of having a research program focused on the national security implications of the Information Age. It develops the theoretical foundations to provide DoD with information superiority and highlights the importance of active outreach and dissemination initiatives designed to acquaint senior military personnel and civilians with these emerging issues. The CCRP Publication Series is a key element of this effort.

Check our Web site for the latest CCRP activities and publications.

www.dodccrp.org

DoD Command and Control Research Program

ASSISTANT SECRETARY OF DEFENSE (NII)
&
CHIEF INFORMATION OFFICER

Dr. Linton Wells, II (Acting)

PRINCIPAL DEPUTY ASSISTANT SECRETARY OF DEFENSE (NII)

Dr. Linton Wells, II

SPECIAL ASSISTANT TO THE ASD(NII)
&
DIRECTOR OF RESEARCH

Dr. David S. Alberts

Library of Congress Cataloging-in-Publication Data

Alberts, David S. (David Stephen), 1942-
Code of best practice for experimentation / David S. Alberts, Richard E. Hayes.
   p. cm. -- (CCRP publication series)
Includes bibliographical references.
ISBN 1-893723-07-0 (pbk.)
1. Military research—United States—Methodology. I. Hayes, Richard E., 1942-
   II. Title. III. Series.
U393 .A667 2002
355'.07'0973--dc21
      2002011564

1st printing July 2002
2nd printing October 2003
3rd printing August 2005

C^{ODE} O^F B^{EST} P^{RACTICE}

EXPERIMENTATION

Table of Contents

List of Figures

Acknowledgments

This Code of Best Practice would never have been undertaken if it were not for the inspiration and support provided to this effort by MG Dean Cash. MG Cash, as the J9 at JFCOM, is responsible for joint experimentation. Joint experimentation is an awesome responsibility since it is a critical mission that will directly influence the course of no less than the transformation of the DoD and ultimately our ability to meet the challenges of the new century. MG Cash recognized that experimentation was not yet a core competency and that efforts to better understand how experiments should be planned, conducted, and mined for insights were key to the success of his organization's mission. Driven by a desire not only to record lessons from past experimenters but also to ensure the quality of future ones, he requested that the CCRP engage the best minds we could employ to develop this Code of Best Practice (COBP) for Experimentation.

The COBP is not being published as a definitive work. Much remains to be learned about organizing and conducting experiments of the extraordinary range and complexity required by the task of transformation. Rather, this code should be seen for what it is- an initial effort to pull together important basic ideas and the myriad lessons learned from previous experiments and to synthesize this material into a guide for those who must conceive, plan, conduct, and analyze the results of experiments as well as those who must use the results of experimentation to make decisions about the future of the military.

Many people contributed to this effort. We undertook the roles of contributing editors, trying to ensure both coherence and coverage of key topics. John E. Kirzl, Dr. Dennis K. Leedom, and Dr. Daniel T. Maxwell each drafted important elements of the volume. Significant and very helpful comments on an early draft were received from Dr. Larry Wiener and Dr. Richard Kass. A debt of gratitude is also owed to the members of the AIAA Technical Committee on Information and C2 Systems who contributed to a forerunner to the COBP, a study of lessons learned from the first Joint Expeditionary Force Experiment (JEFX). This review was requested of them by the then J7 MGen Close. Participating with us in the AIAA study were John Baird, John Buchheister, Dr. Leland Joe, Kenneth L. Jordan, Dr. Alexander H. Levis, Dr. Russel Richards, RADM Gary Wheatley (ret), and Dr. Cindy L. Williams. In some important ways, this document also builds upon the NATO *COBP of C2 Assessment*, a product of an outstanding international team. Participating with us in the SAS-026 effort were Dr. Alexander von Baeyer, Timothy Bailey, Paul Choinard, Dr. Uwe Dompke, Cornelius d'Huy, Dr. Dean Hartley, Dr. Reiner Huber, Donald Kroening, Dr. Stef Kurstjens, Nicholas Lambert, Dr. Georges Lascar, LtCol (ret) Christian Manac'h, Graham Mathieson, Prof. James Moffat, Lt. Orhun Molyer, Valdur Pille, Mark Sinclair, Mink Spaans, Dr. Stuart Starr, Dr. Swen Stoop, Hans Olav Sundfor, LtCol Klaus Titze, Dr. Andreas Tolk, Corinne Wallshein, and John Wilder.

The Information Superiority Working Group (ISWG), a voluntary group of professionals from government, industry, and academia that meets monthly under CCRP leadership to further the state of the art and practice, also contributed significant ideas. Members of the ISWG include Edgar Bates, Dr. Peter Brooks, Dennis Damiens, Hank DeMattia, Greg Giovanis, Dr. Paul Hiniker, Hans Keithley, Dr. Cliff Lieberman, Julia Loughran, Dr. Mark Mandeles, Telyvin Murphy, Dan Oertel, Dr. Walter Perry, John Poirier, Dennis Popiela, Steve Shaker, Dr. David Signori, Dr. Ed Smith, Marcy Stahl, Chuck Taylor, Mitzi Wertheim, Dave White, and Dr. Larry Wiener.

I would also like to thank Joseph Lewis for editing our rough drafts into a finished product and Bernie Pineau for designing and producing the graphics, charts, and cover artwork.

Dr. David S. Alberts   Dr. Richard E. Hayes

Preface

Experimentation is the lynch pin in the DoD's strategy for transformation. Without a properly focused, well-balanced, rigorously designed, and expertly conducted program of experimentation, the DoD will not be able to take full advantage of the opportunities that Information Age concepts and technologies offer.

Therefore, experimentation needs to become a new DoD core competency and assume its rightful place along side of our already world-class training and exercise capabilities. In fact, as we gain experience and acquire expertise with the design and conduct of experiments and focused experimentation campaigns, I expect that the way in which we think about and conduct training and exercises will become a coherent continuum within the overall process of coevolving new mission capability packages.

This Code of Best Practice was developed to (1) accelerate the process of our becoming more aware of the issues involved in planning, designing, and conducting experiments and using experiment results, and (2) provide support to individuals and organizations engaged in a variety of experimentation activities in support of DoD transformation.

This initial edition of the Code of Best Practice will evolve over time as we gain more experience and incorporate that experience into new versions of the

Code. We are interested in learning about your reactions to this Code, your suggestions for improving the Code, and your experiences with experimentation. For this purpose, a form has been provided in the back of the Code for you.

CHAPTER 1

Introduction

Why DoD Experiments?

Experiments of various kinds have begun to proliferate throughout the Department of Defense (DoD) as interest in transforming the defense capabilities of the United States has grown. DoD transformation is motivated by a recognition that (1) the national security environment of the 21st century will be significantly different and as a consequence, the roles and missions the nation will call upon the DoD to undertake will require new competencies and capabilities, (2) Information Age concepts and technologies provide unparalleled opportunities to develop and employ new operational concepts that promise to dramatically enhance competitive advantage, and (3) the DoD's business processes will need to adapt to provide the flexibility and speed necessary to keep pace with the rapid changes in both our national security and information-related technologies, as well as the organizational adaptations associated with these advances.

Need For a Code of Best Practice

There is growing concern that many of the activities labeled *experiments* being conducted by the DoD have been less valuable than they could have been. That is, their contributions to DoD strategies and decisions, to the development of mission capability packages (MCPs), and to the body of knowledge in general have been limited by the manner in which they have been conceived and conducted. Given the prominent role that both joint and Service experimentation need to play in the transformation of the DoD, it seems reasonable to ask if we can do better. We believe that the answer is a resounding "yes."

This Code of Best Practice (COBP) is intended to (1) increase awareness and understanding of the different types of experimentation activities that the DoD needs to employ in order to inform the transformation, (2) articulate a useful set of organizing principles for the design and conduct of experiments and experimentation campaigns, (3) provide both producers of experiments and consumers of experimentation results with "best practice" and lessons learned, (4) provide future experimenters with a firm foundation upon which to build, and (5) promote a degree of scientific rigor and professionalism in the DoD experimentation process.

Scope and Focus

This COBP presents a philosophy and broad set of guidelines to be considered by professionals responsible for planning and conducting experiments within the DoD, and by policy makers who must judge the validity of experimentation insights and incorporate them into defense policy and investment decisions.

The DoD transformation has three dimensions: what we do; how we do it; and how we provision and prepare. Experimentation activities are and will be focused on each of these three dimensions. This COBP is intended to apply across all three dimensions, but particularly upon the second of these dimensions – how we do it – and uses the precepts and hypotheses of Network Centric Warfare (NCW) to explore each of the facets of experimentation. Additionally, the Code presents examples and discussions that highlight why adherence to sound experimentation principles is important.

Organization of the Code

To effectively illuminate the many aspects and stages of experimentation, this Code of Best Practice proceeds from broad to specific topics, as well as studying the stages of experimentation as they occur chronologically.

Chapter 2 briefly discusses the need for a DoD transformation in the context of the military and political agendas at the time of this writing. To support transformation efforts, the need for superior experimentation techniques and processes are introduced. Chapter 3 provides a definition and overview of experimentation, both as a general concept and a DoD process. The three uses of experimentation (discovery, hypothesis testing, and demonstration) are defined and differentiated by their roles within the DoD.

Chapter 4 explains the need and purpose for experimentation campaigns, as opposed to focusing only on individual experiments. Since the purpose of any experiment should be to increase or generate useful knowledge, it must also be the purpose of the experiment to ensure the validity of that knowledge. Because no individual experiment, regardless of preparation and execution, is immune from human error or the effects of unforeseeable variables, multiple experiments must be conducted to verify results.

In Chapter 5, the anatomy of an experiment is broken down into phases, stages, and cycles of interaction. By understanding the purpose of each stage of the experiment (and its relationships to other stages), the experimentation team can conduct a more profitable experiment through proper preparation, execution, feedback, and analysis. An incomplete execution of the experimentation process can only result in an incomplete experiment with weak products. Experimentation formulation is discussed in Chapter 6. This begins with a discussion of how to formulate an experimentation issue and proceeds to a short discussion of specific experimentation design considerations.

Chapter 7, Metrics and Measures, examines the need for generating and specifying the metrics and measures to be used in the data collection process, including the need to ensure that team members use identical definitions of terms and metrics. Chapter 8 discusses the importance of properly designing and employing a set of scenarios[1] that provide an opportunity to observe a range of values for the variables of interest.

Chapter 9 discusses the importance of developing and implementing data analysis and data collection plans, both before and during the conduct of the experiment to ensure that all needed data are properly identified, collected, and archived, and that they remain available for future use. The actual conduct and execution of the experiment is reviewed in Chapter 10.

The generation of a set of products (as discussed in Chapter 11) is crucial to the dissemination of the experimentation results to the sponsors and the research community. Chapter 12 discusses the uses, benefits, and limitations of modeling and simulation as a substitute for empirical data collection. Chapter 13 concludes this Code with a discussion of the most common failures and obstacles to successful experimentation.

―――――――――――――

[1]The American use of the word "scenario" is interchangeable with the British "usecase."

CHAPTER 2

Transformation and Experimentation

Transformation and NCW

Our transformational challenge is clear. In the words of the President, "We must build forces that draw upon the revolutionary advances in the technology of war...one that relies more heavily on stealth, precision, weaponry, and *information technologies*" (emphasis added). Information technologies have proven to be revolutionary not only in the nature of the capabilities being developed in the "Information Domain"[1] and the pace of these advances, but also in promoting discontinuous changes in the way individuals and organizations create effects, accomplish their tasks, and realize their objectives. The DoD's *Network Centric Warfare Report to Congress*[2] defines the connection between DoD Transformation and Network Centric Warfare: "Network Centric Warfare (NCW) is no less than the embodiment of an Information Age transformation of the DoD. It involves a new way of thinking about how we accomplish our missions, how we organize and

7

interrelate, and how we acquire and field the systems that support us... It will involve ways of operating that have yet to be conceived, and will employ technologies yet to be invented... This view of the future is supported by accumulating evidence from a wide variety of experiments, exercises, simulations, and analyses."[3]

NCW and Experimentation

The report goes on to explain NCW in terms of a set of tenets that are, in essence, a set of linkage hypotheses that provide structure and guidance for the development of network-centric operational concepts. These tenets serve as a useful set of organizing principles for experimentation. Thus, DoD experiments should focus on exploring the basic tenets of NCW, and developing and maturing network-centric operational concepts based upon these tenets.

Tenets of NCW

NCW represents a powerful set of warfighting concepts and associated military capabilities that allow warfighters to take full advantage of all available information and bring all available assets to bear in a rapid and flexible manner. The four tenets of NCW are that:

- A robustly networked force improves information sharing and collaboration;

- Information sharing and collaboration enhance the quality of information and shared situational awareness;

- Shared situational awareness enables self-synchronization; and

- These, in turn, dramatically increase mission effectiveness.

Each tenet represents a testable linkage hypothesis. The tenets themselves are linked to form a value chain as shown in Figure 2-1.

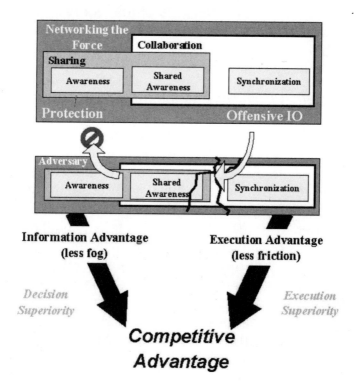

Figure 2-1. NCW Value Chain

The Domains of NCW

NCW concepts can only be understood and explored by focusing on the relationships that take place simultaneously in and among the *physical*, *information*, and *cognitive* domains.

Physical Domain: The physical domain is the traditional domain of warfare. It is where strike, protection, and maneuver operations take place across the ground, sea, air, and space environments. It is the domain where physical platforms and the communications networks that connect them reside. Comparatively, the elements of this domain are the easiest to "see" and to measure; consequently, combat power has traditionally been measured by effects in this domain.

Information Domain: The information domain is the domain where information is created, manipulated, and shared. Moreover, it is the domain where the command and control of modern military forces is communicated and where a commander's intent is conveyed. Consequently, it is increasingly the information domain that must be protected and defended to enable a force to generate combat power in the face of offensive actions taken by an adversary. And, in the all-important battle for information superiority, the information domain is the area of greatest sensitivity. System performance related metrics (e.g., bandwidths) have predominated until recently, but these are no longer sufficient by themselves for measuring the quality of information.

Cognitive Domain: The cognitive domain is the domain of the mind of the warfighter and the warfighter's supporting populace. This is the domain where commander's intent, doctrine, tactics, techniques, and procedures reside. The intangibles of leadership, morale, unit cohesion, level of training and experience, situation awareness, and public opinion are elements of this domain. Effects in this domain present the greatest challenge with respect to observation and measurement.

A warfighting force that can conduct network-centric operations can be defined as having the following command and control-related attributes and capabilities in each of the domains:

Physical Domain

- All elements of the force are robustly networked, achieving secure and seamless connectivity, or

- Sufficient resources are present to dominate the physical domain using NCW-derived information advantage.

Information Domain

- The force has the capability to collect, share, access, and protect information.

- The force has the capability to collaborate, which enables it to improve its information position through processes of correlation, fusion, and analysis.

- A force can achieve information advantage over an adversary.

Cognitive Domain

- The force is able to develop and share high-quality situation awareness.

- The force is able to develop a shared knowledge of the commander's intent.

- The force is able to self-synchronize its operations.

Experimentation with the application of network-centric operational concepts should be traceable directly to one or more of the linkage hypotheses or to one or more of the attributes and capabilities that define network-centric operations. Thus, there will need to be experiments that involve attention to all three of the domains and the interactions among them.

Concept-Based, Mission Capability-Focused Experimentation

NCW involves changes not only in information-related capabilities and flows, but also in the way decisions and processes are distributed across the force. It has long been understood that, in order to leverage increases in information-related capabilities, new ways of doing business are required.

This is not just a matter of getting the most out of new information-related capabilities, but these new ways of doing business are needed to avoid potential organizational dysfunction. This idea is explored in

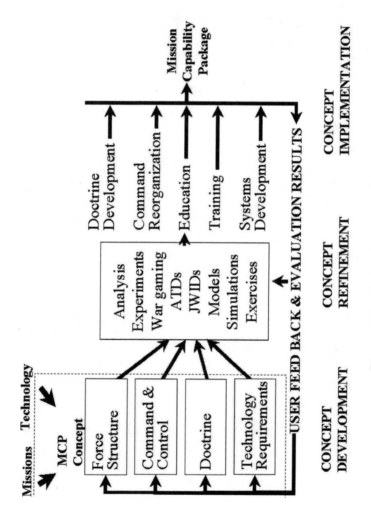

Figure 2-2. Mission Capability Packages

the book *Unintended Consequences of the Information Age*. It addresses the concept of mission capability packages as a framework for dealing with the introduction of new technology (Figure 2-2).

Thus, the essence of a network-centric capability is a coevolved mission capability package, one that derives its power from the tenets of NCW. A mission capability package begins with a concept of operations, in this case a network-centric concept of operations that includes characteristics from each of the domains described above.

Note that NCW applications exist at different levels of maturity. For example, a less mature application may only seek to share information to improve the quality of information available to the participants; it would not involve changes to process or command approach. Conversely, a fully mature network-centric concept would involve collaboration and a command approach that features self-synchronization. The NCW Report to Congress provides a maturity model (Figure 2-3) that defines a migration path for the maturing of NCW capabilities over time and hence, a migration path for experimentation.

Command and Control

		Traditional	Collaborative Planning	Self-synchronization
Developing Situation Awareness	Shared Awareness		3	4
	Information Sharing	1	2	
	Organic Sources	0		

Figure 2-3. NCW Maturity Model

The "guts" of the network-centric mission capability package consists of three components:

- An approach to command and control that is designed to leverage shared awareness;

- An organizational form that fosters information sharing and collaboration; and

- Doctrine, with associated technology, tactics, techniques, and procedures.

The information and systems capability necessary to support the required level of shared awareness must be combined with the expertise, experience, and skills of the people, materials, and systems necessary to support them and carry out the mission. Taken together, this constitutes a mission capability package. All of this is required to turn an operational concept into a real deployable capability.

The term *mission capability package* is preferred to the widely used acronym DOTMLPF (doctrine, organization, training, material, leadership, personnel, and facilities) because it is broader. A mission capability package, or the innovation it represents, certainly can impact and must take into account all the elements of DOTMLPF, but it is also richer (may have more than one form while under development) and matures over time as the mission capability package process is executed. Hence, the innovation "collaborative work process" may take several different forms depending on the function being performed and may be supported by an evolving set of DOTMLPF elements as it matures.

The objectives of experimentation are therefore to develop and refine innovative concepts of operation and to coevolve mission capability packages to turn these concepts into real operational capabilities. One experiment cannot possibly achieve this objective. Rather it will take a well-orchestrated experimentation campaign consisting of a series of related activities to accomplish this. Hence, this COBP treats both how to conduct successful individual experiments and also how to link them together into successful campaigns of experimentation.

---

[1]Alberts, David S., John J. Garstka, and Frederick P. Stein. *Network Centric Warfare: Developing and Leveraging Information Superiority*. Second Edition. Washington, DC: CCRP. 1999.

²*Network Centric Warfare Department of Defense Report to Congress.* July 2001.
³Ibid. Executive Summary, p. i.

CHAPTER 3

Overview of Experimentation

The term *experimentation* arises from the Latin, experiri, which means, "to try." Experimentation knowledge differs from other types of knowledge in that it is always founded upon observation or experience. In other words, experiments are always empirical. However, measurement alone does not make an experiment. Experiments also involve establishing some level of control and also manipulating one or more factors of interest in order to establish or track cause and effect. A dictionary definition of *experiment* is a test made "to determine the efficacy of something previously untried," "to examine the validity of an hypothesis," or "to demonstrate a known truth." These three meanings distinguish the three major roles that DoD organizations have assigned to experimentation.

Uses of Experiments

Discovery experiments involve introducing novel systems, concepts, organizational structures, technologies, or other elements to a setting where their use can be observed and catalogued. In the DoD context, the objective is to find out how the innovation is employed and whether it appears to have military utility. Discovery experiments are similar to the time honored military practice by which new military hardware (aircraft, tanks, etc.) was developed against a set of technical specifications (fly faster, turn tighter, shoot farther, etc.), then given to technical user communities (typically Service test organizations or boards) to work out the concepts of operation, tactics, techniques, and procedure for effective employment. For example, when GPS was a novel concept, one U.S. Marine Corps battalion was reportedly provided with the capability and given a few days to decide how they might best employ it, then run through the standard 29 Palms exercise to see both how they used the capability and what difference it made. This discovery experiment was enabled because a body of knowledge existed on how U.S. Marine Corps battalions performed the 29 Palms mission, so the sentry GPS was a manipulation and the 29 Palms setting and U.S.M.C. organization were, effectively, controls.

The goals of discovery experiments are to identify potential military benefits, generate ideas about the best way for the innovation to be employed, and identify the conditions under which it can be used (as well as the limiting conditions – situations where the benefits may not be available). In a scientific sense, these are "hypothesis generation" efforts. They will typically be employed early in the development cycle. While these experiments must be observed carefully and empirically in order to generate rich insights and knowledge, they will not ordinarily provide enough information (or evidence) to reach a conclusion that is valid (correct understandings of the cause-and-effect or temporal relationships that are hypothesized) or reliable (can be recreated in another experimentation setting). They are typically guided by some clearly innovative propositions (see Chapters 5 and 6) that would be understood as hypotheses if there were a body of existing knowledge that supported them. Typical discovery experiments lack the degree of control necessary to infer cause and effect, and often involve too few cases or trials to support valid statistical inference.

However, these limitations are not barriers to discovery experimentation. Most new concepts, ideas, and technologies will benefit from discovery experimentation as a way of weeding out ideas that simply do not work, forcing the community to ask rigorous questions about the benefits being sought and the dynamics involved in implementing the idea, or specifying the limiting conditions for the innovation. Good discovery experiments will lay the foundation for more rigorous types of experiments where the hypotheses they generate are subject to more rigorous assessment and refinement.

Moreover, discovery experiments must be observed in detail if they are to reach their maximum value. For example, one of the earliest discovery experiments looking at Joint Vision 2010 concepts found that the subjects altered their working organization and process during the event. This was reported as a major finding. However, no tools or instruments were in place to record how the players altered their processes and structures, so the experiment fell short of specifying precise hypotheses to guide later research and development.

Hypothesis testing experiments are the classic type used by scholars to advance knowledge by seeking to falsify specific hypotheses (specifically if...then statements) or discover their limiting conditions. They are also used to test whole theories (systems of consistent, related hypotheses that attempt to explain some domain of knowledge) or observable hypotheses derived from such theories. In a scientific sense, hypothesis testing experiments build knowledge or refine our understanding of a knowledge domain.

In order to conduct hypothesis testing experiments, the experimenter(s) create a situation in which one or more factors of interest (dependent variables) can be observed systematically under conditions that vary the values of factors thought to cause change (independent variables) in the factors of interest, while other potentially relevant factors (control variables) are held constant, either empirically or through statistical manipulation. Hence, results from hypothesis testing experiments are always caveated with ceteris paribus, or "all other things being equal." Both control and manipulation are integral to formulating hypothesis testing experiments.

Hypothesis testing experiments have been employed in a variety of military settings. For example, DARPA's Command Post of the Future (CPOF) Program ran an experiment on alternative presentation technologies and their impact on the situation awareness of individuals. Similarly, the J-9, JFCOM

Experimentation Command ran an experiment on presentation technologies and their impact on individual and team situation awareness.

Since the number of independent, dependent, and control variables relevant in the military arena is very large, considerable thought and care are often needed to conduct valid hypothesis tests. Moreover, no single experiment is likely to do more than improve knowledge marginally and help clarify new issues. Hence, sets of related hypothesis testing experiments are often needed in order to gain useful knowledge. The planning of sets of related experiments is discussed below under the heading of experimentation campaigns.

Demonstration experiments, in which known truth is recreated, are analogous to the experiments conducted in a high school, where students follow instructions that help them prove to themselves that the laws of chemistry and physics operate as the underlying theories predict. DoD equivalent activities are technology demonstrations used to show operational organizations that some innovation can, under carefully orchestrated conditions, improve the efficiency, effectiveness, or speed of a military activity. In such demonstrations, all the technologies employed are well-established and the setting (scenario, participants, etc.) is orchestrated to show that these technologies can be employed efficiently and effectively under the specified conditions.

Note that demonstration experiments are not intended to generate new knowledge, but rather to display existing knowledge to people unfamiliar with it. The reasons for empirical observation change to recording the results reliably and noting the conditions under which the innovations were demonstrated in demonstration experiments. Failure to capture this information will lead to unrealistic expectations and inappropriate applications of the innovations. This has happened more than once in the DoD when capabilities developed for a specific demonstration were transferred to a very different context and failed because they had not been properly adapted. Some demonstration experiments involve control, but no manipulation.

Experimentation Campaigns

As noted earlier, military operations are too complex and the process of change is too expensive for the U.S. to rely on any single experiment to "prove" that a particular innovation should be adopted or will provide a well-understood set of military benefits. Indeed, in academic settings, no single experiment is relied on to create new knowledge. Instead, scholars expect that experimentation results will be repeatable and will fit into a pattern of knowledge on related topics. Replication is important because it demonstrates that the experimentation results are not the product of some particular circumstances (selection of subjects, choice of the experimentation situation or scenario, bias of the researchers, etc.). Placing the results in the context of other research and experimentation provides reasons to believe that the results are valid and also help to provide linkages to the causal mechanisms at work.

An experimentation campaign is a series of related activities that explore and mature knowledge about a concept of interest. As illustrated in Figure 3-1, experimentation campaigns use the different types of experiments in a logical way to move from an idea or concept to some demonstrated military capability. Hence, experimentation campaigns are organized ways of testing innovations that allow refinement and support increased understanding over time.

The *initial concept* may come from almost anywhere – a technological innovation, a concept of operations developed to deal with new or emerging threats, a capability that has emerged in civilian practice and appears to have meaningful military application and utility, a commission or study generated to examine a problem, lessons learned from a conflict, an observed innovation in a foreign force, or any of a host of other sources.

Ideally, this innovation is understood well enough to place it in the context of a mission capability package. For example, a technological innovation may require new doctrine, organizational structures, training, or other support in order to achieve the military utility envisioned for it. In some cases, research into prior experience, applications, or research on similar topics may help development of the mission capability package needed. Simply placing a technological innovation into the context of existing doctrine, organization, and training for discovery experimentation is normally a very weak and inefficient approach for it will not be able to properly evaluate the potential of the technological innovation. In cases where this has been done, the

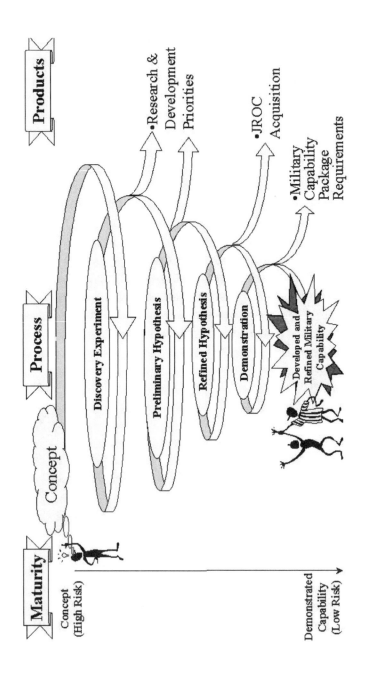

Figure 3-1. From Theory to Practice

potential value of the innovation has been missed or undervalued.

Discovery Experiments in the Context of an Experimentation Campaign

Obviously, some discovery experiments will be needed first to see whether the innovation shows serious potential for military utility and impact. These may involve pure models and computer simulations to place the new concept in the context of other factors, or human-in-the-loop experiments to learn how people relate to the innovation and choose to employ it, or war games, or field trials. Whatever formats are chosen should be loosely configured to encourage adaptation and innovation, but should also be carefully observed, recorded, and analyzed to maximize learning. In many cases, these discovery experiments will involve surrogate capabilities that create the effect of the innovation, but minimize the cost of the effort.

Perhaps the most famous initial discovery experiments were those conducted by the Germans to explore the tactical use of short range radios before World War II. They mimicked a battlespace (using Volkswagens as tanks) in order to learn about the reliability of the radios and the best way to employ the new communications capabilities and information exchanges among the components of their force. Similarly, the early U.S. Marine Corps experimentation with remotely piloted vehicles (RPVs) during efforts like HUNTER WARRIOR used commercially available vehicles to conduct a variety of missions, from reconnaissance to resupply. In both cases, the users were able to gain a basic understanding of the potential uses and limits of novel technologies. This prepared them for more rigorous and focused development and testing later. Similarly, the Command Post of the Future program in DARPA has conducted a series of "block party" experiments in which their technologists have worked together with selected military subject matter experts (SMEs) to try out new technologies across a variety of military contexts, ranging from meeting engagements to urban warfare. An interesting discovery experiment was generated by the Air Force in 1994 and 1995 when Lieutenant General Edward Franklin, U.S. Air Force, then head of the U.S. Air Force ESC (Electronic Systems Center) at Hanscom Air Force Base, required that all Air Force command and control-related programs set up shop at the end of one of his runways and demonstrate their capability for interoperability with other systems funded by the Air Force. A great deal of discovery occurred as program managers and contractors struggled to meet this requirement.

Note that not all discovery experiments result in enough knowledge gain to support moving to the hypothesis testing level. One major advantage of an experimentation perspective is that some ideas do not prove sound, at least as presently conceived and understood. Hence, Figure 3-1 shows the results of some discovery experiments as simply establishing new research and development priorities. In other words, if there was a real opportunity or a real problem being addressed during the discovery experiment, but the proposed innovation did not look promising in the experimentation setting, then some different approach would be needed. This approach may be a new innovation, some change to another element of the mission capability package, or recognition of a limiting condition not previously understood. In many cases, further discovery experimentation may also be needed.

Even when an initial discovery experiment is successful in suggesting military utility and some way of employing the innovation, more research and discovery experimentation will usually be required to validate the initial finding, to refine the employment concepts, or to determine the conditions under which the innovation is most likely to provide significant payoff. At a minimum, the results of an apparently successful discovery experiment needs to be exposed to the widest possible community, including operators and other researchers. This breadth of exposure is an inherent part of the scientific method being harnessed for experimentation. It ensures that constructive criticism will be offered, alternative explanations for the findings will be explored, and the related research will be identified. In many cases, it will also spark other research and experimentation intended to replicate and validate the initial findings. The more important the innovation and the higher the potential payoff, the greater the community's interest and the more likely the discovery experiment will be replicated or created in a somewhat different domain. All this greatly benefits the processes of maturing the concept and developing improved knowledge.

Hypothesis Testing Experiments in the Context of an Experimentation Campaign

When the discovery experimentation process has produced interesting, important, and well-stated hypotheses, the experimentation campaign is ready to move to a hypothesis testing stage. Figure 3-1 stresses that this is a complex stage, highlighting the idea that there will be both preliminary and refined hypothesis tests as the innovation matures and becomes better understood.

Technically speaking, no hypothesis is ever proven. The strongest statement that a scientist can make is that the evidence is consistent with (supports) a given hypothesis. However, propositions can be disproved by the discovery of evidence inconsistent with them. To take a simple example, the proposition that the world is flat was disproved by the observation that when ships sailed away from port, their hulls disappeared before their sails. However, that observation could not prove the world was round. The idea that the world was curved, but still had an edge, was also consistent with the evidence.

Science therefore uses the very useful concept of a *null hypothesis*, which is stated as the converse of the hypothesis being tested. Experimenters then attempt to obtain sufficient evidence to disprove the null hypothesis. This provides supporting evidence for the original hypothesis, although it does not prove it. For example, in Command Post of the Future experimentation with visualization technologies, the hypothesis was that:

IF sets of tailored visualizations were presented to subjects, THEN those subjects would have richer situation awareness than those subjects presented with standard military maps and symbols, UNDER THE CONDITIONS THAT the same underlying information was available to those creating both types of displays, the subjects were active duty military officers with at least 10 years of service, and the subjects' time to absorb the material was limited.

This proposition could not be proven, so the more useful null hypothesis was crafted:

IF sets of tailored visualizations were presented to subjects, THEN *no improvement* would be observed in the richness of their situation awareness than that of subjects presented with standard military maps and symbols, UNDER THE CONDITIONS THAT the same underlying information was available to those creating both types of displays, the subjects were active duty military officers with at least 10 years of service, and the subjects' time to absorb the material was limited.

When significant differences were reported, the null hypothesis was rejected and the evidence was found to be consistent with the primary hypothesis. Experimentation and research could then move on to replicating the findings with different subjects in different experimentation settings, and specifying which elements in the tailored visualization were generating which parts of the richer situation awareness. Hence, the experimentation campaign was advanced, but by no means concluded, by the hypothesis testing experiment.

Selecting the hypothesis to be examined in an experiment is a crucial and sometimes difficult task. The innovation and its expected impact need to be defined clearly. Moreover, establishing a baseline – how this task is carried out in the absence of the innovation – is a crucial element. If the hypotheses are not set up for comparative purposes, the experiment will contribute little to the knowledge domain. For example, demonstrating that a new collaborative process can be used to support mission planning is not very helpful unless the hypothesis is drawn to compare this new process with an existing one. Failure to establish the baseline leaves an open question of whether any benefit is achieved by the innovation.

Several rounds of hypothesis testing experiments are needed for any reasonably complex or important mission capability package. The variety of applicable military contexts and the rich variety of human behavior and cognition argue for care during this process. Many innovations currently of interest, such as collaborative work processes and dispersed headquarters, have so many different applications that they must be studied in a variety of contexts. Others have organizational and cultural implications that must be examined in coalition, interagency, and international contexts.

As Figure 3-1 shows, some hypothesis testing experiments also result in spinning off research and development issues or helping to establish priorities for them. In other words, some experiments will identify anomalies that require research, others will suggest new innovations, and still others will identify missing elements that must be researched and understood before the innovation can be implemented successfully.

Particularly visible sets of hypothesis testing propositions are the Limited Objective Experiments (LOEs) being undertaken by J-9, JFCOM. They have scheduled a series of hypothesis testing experiments focused on specific elements of their new concepts, having recognized that there are a variety of issues contained in the innovative concepts they are developing. Their major events, such as Millennium Challenge '02 and Olympic Challenge '04, are both too large and complex to effectively determine the cause and effect relationships involved in the large number of innovations they encompass. For example, during 2001 they ran LOEs on the value of open source information, alternative presentation technologies, coalition processes, and production of their key documents (Operational Net Assessments and Effects Tasking Orders). Similarly, the U.S. Navy's series of Fleet Battle Experiments have each sought to examine some specific element of Network Centric Warfare in order to understand their uses and limits.

Early or preliminary hypothesis testing experiments often lead to more than one "spiral" of more refined hypothesis testing experiments as a fundamental concept or idea is placed into different application contexts. This is a natural process that is furthered by widely reporting the results of the early experiments, thereby attracting the attention of experts in different application arenas. For example, good ideas arising from the Revolution in Business Affairs are being explored in a variety of DoD arenas, from military medicine and personnel to force deployment and sustainment. Each of these arenas has different cultures, experiences, limiting conditions, and organizational structures, so no single line of experimentation is likely to provide satisfactory knowledge to all of them. Rich innovations can be expected to generate multiple experimentation campaigns.

Once an experimentation campaign has refined the community's understanding of an innovation, its uses and limits, and the benefits available from it, it is ready to move into the formal acquisition or adoption processes. As Figure 3-1 indicates, a well-crafted campaign, conducted in the context of a meaningful community discussion, should provide the evidence needed for JROC or other formal assessment and budgetary support. This does, however, presuppose high-quality experiments, widely reported so that the relevant military community understands the results and findings that indicate military utility.

Demonstration Experiments in the Context of an Experimentation Campaign

Many innovations fail to attract sufficient support to move directly into the acquisition or adoption processes. This can occur for a variety of reasons, but often involves inadequate awareness, skepticism, or lack of confidence in the user communities. Faced with these situations, program managers have sometimes found it valuable to perform demonstration experiments, where they can display the value of their innovation to operators. Indeed, both Technology Demonstrations (TDs) and Advanced Concept Technology Demonstrations (ACTDs) have proven increasingly valuable over the past decade.

To be useful, demonstration experiments must place technologies or other innovations into a specific context developed in order to demonstrate their utility. They can only be done effectively and efficiently with well-developed innovations that have been subjected to enough discovery and hypothesis testing experimentation to identify the types of military utility available, to define the context within which those benefits can be realized, and to identify the other elements of the mission capability package necessary for successful application. If these criteria are ignored, the demonstration experiment will quickly degenerate into an ad hoc assembly of items optimized on a very narrow problem, proving unconvincing to the operators for whom it is designed, and unable to support more general application after the demonstration.

As noted earlier, demonstration experiments also need to be observed and instrumented so that the benefits being demonstrated are documented and can be recalled after the experiment is over. Failure to capture the empirical evidence of a successful demonstration experiment turns it into simple "show and tell" and prevents carrying the results to audiences that were not present during the event. This may be particularly important if funding support is being sought for the innovation. Endorsements from senior officers and their staffs are valuable, but not persuasive in budget contests where every item comes with a cadre of supporters, usually from the part of the community that is perceived as having a vested interest in the innovation.

Results of a Well-Crafted Experimentation Campaign

Properly designed and executed, experimentation campaigns generate several useful products. These include:

- A richly crafted mission capability package that clearly defines the innovation and the elements necessary for its success;

- A set of research results that form a coherent whole and specify how the innovation should be implemented, the cause and effect relationships at work, the conditions necessary for success, and the types of military benefits that can be anticipated;

- A community of interest that includes researchers, operators, and decisionmakers who understand the innovation and are in a position to assess its value; and

- Massive reduction in the risks associated with adopting an innovation.

An Experimentation Venue is Not an Experimentation Campaign

Over the past several years, a few military organizations have lost sight of the complexity of conducting experiments and sought to create large exercises in which a variety of different experiments can be conducted. These integrated constructs have almost always been at least partially field exercises, often in the context of major command post exercises. The underlying idea is to generate some efficiencies in terms of the scenarios being employed, the missions and tasks assigned, and the personnel involved. Good examples include the U.S. Air Force series known as JEFX (Joint Expeditionary Force Exercise) and the U.S. Marine Corps series of HUNTER exercises. These integrated constructs should be understood to be experimentation *venues* because they create an opportunity to conduct a variety of different experiments. However, they are not experimentation campaigns because they typically include experiments about different domains.

While large experimentation venues do provide the opportunity for a variety of specific experiments, they also can present unique challenges. For example, different experiments may be interlocked, with the independent or intervening variables for one experiment (which are deliberately controlled) being or impacting on the dependent variable for another. Similarly, many of these experimentation venues are, at least in part, training exercises for the forces they field. This can mean that current doctrine and organization, which may differ substantially from those identified in the mission capability package, play a controlling role. It can also limit the availability of the experiment subjects for training.

Core Challenges of Experimentation

The core challenges of good experimentation are no different for the DoD than any other group seeking to refine and mature a concept or an innovation. They include:

- Clear specification of the idea;

- Creation of a mission capability package that articulates the whole context necessary for success;

- Articulation of the hypotheses underlying the innovation, including the causal mechanisms perceived to make it work;

- Specification of the benefits anticipated from the innovation and the conditions under which they can be anticipated;

- Development of reliable and valid measurement of all elements of the hypotheses such that they can be controlled and/or observed in the experimentation setting;

- Design of an experiment or experimentation campaign that provides unambiguous evidence of what has been observed;

- Creation of an experimentation setting (subjects, scenarios, instrumentation, etc.) that provides for an unbiased assessment of the innovations and hypotheses under study;

- Selection of analytic methods that minimize the risks and uncertainties associated with each experiment or experimentation campaign; and

- Creation of a community of interest that cuts across relevant sets of operators, researchers, and decisionmakers.

Meeting these challenges requires thought, planning, and hard work. The chapters that follow deal with elements of these challenges.

CHAPTER 4

The Logic of Experimentation Campaigns

Why Campaigns Rather Than Individual Experiments?

No single experiment, regardless of how well it is organized and executed, improves knowledge enough to support a major goal like transformation. First, building knowledge requires replication. Scientists know that the findings of a single experiment may be a product of some unknown factor that was not controlled, the impact of biases built into the design, or simply the impact of some random variable unlikely to occur again. Hence, they require replication as a standard for building knowledge.

Second, individual experiments are typically focused on a narrow set of issues. However, the stakes are very high in transformation and the experimentation findings required to pursue it will need to be robust, in other words, they must apply across a wide range of situations. While models and simulations can be used to test the limits of individual experiments, they are neither valid enough nor robust enough in themselves to explore the range of conditions relevant to military operations.

Third, experiments are undertaken on the basis of existing knowledge from prior experience, research, and experimentation. In order to understand experimentation findings fully, they must be placed back into that larger context. When that occurs, alternative interpretations and explanations are often identified for the findings of the single experiment. Hence, new experiments are often needed to help us differentiate between these competing hypotheses before we can claim the "actionable knowledge" needed for transformation.

Fourth, the kind of rich and robust explanations and understandings needed to support transformation will almost inevitably include the unhappy phrase, "it depends." In other words, context matters. Hence, individual experiments, which can only look at a small number of different contexts, will need to be calibrated against other experiments and knowledge to ensure that their limiting conditions are properly understood. This is essential if new knowledge is to be applied wisely and appropriately.

Fifth, building useful knowledge, particularly in a complex arena like transformation, often means bringing together different ideas. Findings from individual experiments often need to be brought together in later experiments in order to see how relevant factors interact. Hence, sets of related experiments often yield richer knowledge than the individual events.

Finally, individual experiments are likely to generate some unexpected findings. Because they are unexpected, such findings are both important and interesting. They may be an indication of new knowledge or new limiting conditions. Experimentation campaigns provide the opportunity to explore these novel insights and findings, as well as their implications and limits, in a more structured setting.

Experimentation Campaigns Require a Different Mindset

It is a misconception to think of an experimentation campaign as merely a series of individual experiments that are strung together. As summarized in Figure 4-1, campaigns serve a broader scientific and operational purpose and require different conceptualization and planning.

An experiment typically involves a single event that is designed to address a specific thread of investigation. For example, experiments conducted by the U.S. Army during the past few years have focused on assessing the impact of introducing digital information technology into command and control processes at battalion through corps level. During this same period, separate experiments were conducted to assess the contributions of selected maintenance and logistics enabler technologies to sustain combat forces. In each case, the experiment involved a single thread of investigation. By contrast, an experimentation campaign involves multiple components (e.g., limited objective experiments, integrating experiments, simulation experiments) conducted over a period of time to address multiple axes of investigation. Each of these axes manipulates some specific aspect of force capability (e.g., networking of command and control, precision and agility of weapon systems, reorganization of sustaining operations) while controlling for others. Taken together, however, these axes of investigation contribute to a broader picture of force transformation.

	EXPERIMENT	EXPERIMENTATION CAMPAIGN
Threads of Investigation	Involves a single event or axis of investigation	Involves multiple events and multiple axes of investigation
Organizing Framework	Organized around a set of specific hypotheses	Organized around a broad goal
Analytic Goal	Provides focused testing of specific set of questions	Provides knowledge across broad set of issues
Number of Decision Points	Executes a specific experimental design	Has multiple decision points for refining issues and analyses
Number of Factors	Measures impact of a few factors while controlling others	Assesses relative importance and impact of many factors
Scenarios	Selected to provide best test of specific hypotheses	Examines a range of contexts to develop generalized predictions
Methodology	Employs selected methods and metrics	Employs a broad range of methods

Figure 4-1. Comparison of An Experiment to An Experimentation Campaign

Experimentation campaigns are organized around a broader framework. Whereas individual experiments are organized around a set of specific issues or hypotheses, campaigns are structured to address broad operational concepts. In the case of individual experiments, the specific issues or hypotheses that are under analysis shape every aspect of experiment planning (e.g., development of metrics, scenario, experiment design). The careful planning of a multi-year experimentation campaign must be motivated and shaped by consistent adherence to broad goals and vision statements moving toward transformation.

Experiments and experimentation campaigns also differ in terms of their analytic goals. Experiments are designed to provide objective testing of a focused set of questions (e.g., are communication bandwidth and connectivity associated with improved shared awareness and understanding?). As such, the experiment is tailored to provide the best conditions and methods for testing the specific set of questions. The fundamental planning question for an experiment is: "Are we researching this issue or testing this hypothesis in the best, most objective manner?" By contrast, campaigns respond to a broader analytic goal. Campaigns are designed to provide comprehensive insight across a set of related issues. The focus of campaign planning is to ensure that each important aspect of force capability is addressed and that no critical issues are overlooked. As a result, the various axes of the experimentation campaign employ a range of conditions and methods for investigating different types of issues. The fundamental planning question for an experimentation campaign is: "Are we addressing all of the important aspects of the problem?"

In terms of decision points, experiments typically reflect a single decision to design and execute a specific experiment. From inception to completion, attention is focused on achieving a single, coherent outcome. Experimentation campaigns, on the other hand, contain multiple decision points that provide the opportunity to either refine alternatives or identify emerging issues. As a result, operational attention can shift from event to event, the nature of the analytical questions can evolve, and the experimentation objectives can mature over time as the campaign yields deeper insights into the problem space. Experimentation campaigns are not fixed or static programs. Rather, they should reflect a degree of adaptibility and innovation to accommodate learning over time. Campaign plans must be flexible so that subsequent events are properly focused to provide for the best return on investment.

Given a number of practical and scientific considerations, experiments are designed to measure the impact of a few factors or variables while controlling other influences on system performance to the highest degree possible. In this manner, causality can be isolated and attributed to a relatively small number of factors. In this sense, experiments best reflect the root concept of *analysis*, the systematic understanding of causes and effects. Experimentation campaigns, by contrast, are designed to assess the relative importance and impact of many different factors or variables within the problem space. The objective of the campaign design is to give comprehensive attention to all of the important influences on system performance. In this sense, experimentation campaigns best reflect the root concept of *synthesis*, the systematic integration of causes and effects into improved, actionable knowledge.

Similarly, experiments best achieve their objectives by tailoring scenarios to provide the best set of conditions for assessing selected issues or testing a set of specific hypotheses. Hence, planning attention is focused on identifying elements of the operational scenarios that allow for adequate variability to occur among input and output measures – an analytical requisite for assessing causality. Depending upon the nature and focus of the experiment, the scenarios can vary in echelon (e.g., tactical, operational, strategic), level of complexity (e.g., isolated military functions, joint operations, effects-based operations), or a few levels of outcome measure (e.g., situation awareness, force synchronization, mission effectiveness). By contrast, campaigns are not limited to a single level of detail, single level of complexity, or a few levels of outcome measure. Hence, planning attention should be given to addressing all important influences on system performance through a range of scenarios. In this manner, experimentation campaigns offer a greater possibility of (1) yielding generalized conclusions, (2) identifying regions of greatest performance sensitivity, (3) associating the body of empirical knowledge with the most likely conditions in the real world, and (4) providing robust insight into transformation-related programming and policy decisions.

Finally, as compared with individual experiments, experimentation campaigns require a broader and more consistent set of performance metrics. A broader set of metrics is required because campaigns typically deal with a more diverse set of military functions, operational effects, and levels of system outcome, as compared with focused experiments. At the same time, however, the set of metrics adopted within a campaign must be defined more consistently from the outset since they are the principal mechanism for linking empirical findings across different experiments. While developing appropriate metrics for an individual experiment is difficult enough, the development of metrics for use in an experimentation campaign requires even more thought and skill in order to anticipate how those metrics will be employed.

Structure Underlying Experimentation Campaigns

As illustrated in Figure 4-2, there are three principle dimensions underlying campaigns of experimentation:

- Maturity of the knowledge contribution – from discovery to hypothesis testing to demonstration;

- Fidelity of experimentation settings – from war gaming to laboratory settings and models to exercises; and

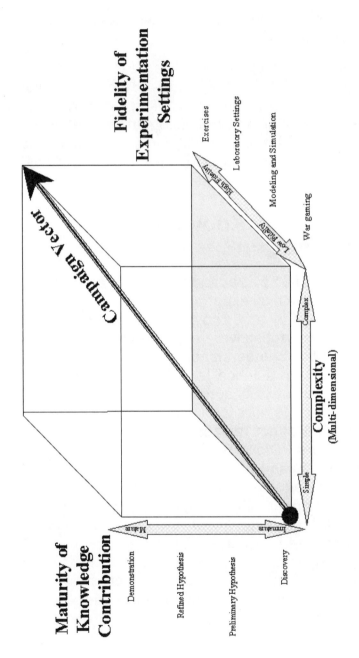

Figure 4-2. The Experimentation Campaign Space

• Complexity of the issues included – from simple to complex.

The logical structure underlying experimentation campaigns is always the same – to move along the "campaign vector" shown in Figure 4-2 from the lower left front of the experimentation space toward the upper right rear. In other words, moving toward more mature knowledge, in more realistic settings, and involving more complex issues.

Maturity of Knowledge Contribution

This dimension was already described as the three basic classes of experiments were introduced. Initial work in any knowledge domain is best undertaken in discovery experiments intended to create a basic understanding of the phenomenon of interest. In science terms, this is an effort to describe what is occurring, classify factors and relevant behaviors correctly, and hypothesize cause and effect relationships and their limiting conditions. Discovery experiments can be designed based on experience, subject matter expertise, prior research, or experimentation on similar or apparently analogous topics. More than one discovery experiment is normally needed to generate the insights and knowledge required to support hypothesis testing experiments. Discovery experiments should also be used to create, refine, and validate the measurement tools needed in the knowledge domain.

Once the hypotheses can be clearly articulated, a series of hypothesis testing experiments can be used to enrich understanding of the issues under study. These typically begin with efforts to refine the hypotheses of interest (in science terms, the set of consistent, interrelated hypotheses that form a theory. However, the term *theory* is seldom used when dealing with experimentation within the DoD because it is understood to convey a sense that the knowledge is tentative or impractical. In fact, there is nothing so practical as a good theory and the set of conditions under which it applies). These initial experiments are typically followed by a number of in-depth experiments that explore alternative cause-and-effect patterns, sets of limiting conditions, and temporal dynamics. Most of the effort necessary to mature knowledge on a given topic will be consumed in these hypothesis testing experiments.

As hypothesis testing experiments go forward, the relevant measures, tools, and techniques needed for successful experimentation are also refined and matured. In addition, by circulating the results of hypothesis testing experiments widely, researchers often generate feedback that enables them to better understand the topics under study. This multiplying effect on knowledge maturity is vital to rapid progress. It allows researchers to learn from both other researchers and also expert practitioners.

Demonstration experiments, which are educational displays of mature knowledge, should not be undertaken until the science underlying the issues of interest have been largely resolved. They can only be done with mature mission capability packages, including technologies, training, organizational structures, and leadership. In essence, the underlying knowledge must be predictive. The cause and effect relationships hypothesized must be fully understood and the conditions necessary for success must be known. Note that demonstration experiments should be few in number and organized primarily to educate potential users of the innovation and those responsible for deciding (1) whether the innovation should be adopted and (2) how the innovation should be resourced. They sometimes also yield knowledge about how the innovation can be employed effectively. The greatest danger in demonstration experimentation is attempting it too soon – when the innovation is immature. Even weakly resourced demonstration experiments using mature innovations are more likely to be successful than premature demonstrations.

Experimentation at different levels of maturity also yields different products. Discovery experiments are intended to weed out ideas that have little chance of success and identify promising ideas. Their products include sets of hypotheses for testing, specification of initial limiting conditions or relevant application contexts, measurement tools, and research and development priorities. Hypothesis testing experiments refine knowledge, sharpen definitions and measures, clarify relationships, improve understanding of limiting conditions, and generate rich insights. They may also help strengthen and focus research and development priorities, particularly in the initial hypothesis testing phase. Well-crafted sets of hypothesis testing experiments can yield the knowledge needed for acquisition efforts, organizational change, and training initiatives. Demonstration experiments are intended to directly support decisions about transformation initiatives.

Fidelity of Experimentation Settings

Mission capability packages and transformation initiatives must ultimately be implemented in the world of real military operations. Their origins, however, are cognitive – concepts arising in someone's mind and developed in dialogue with others. Well-crafted campaigns of experimentation are structured to move from the relatively vague and undisciplined world of ideas and concepts into more and more realistic settings. In the sense of scientific inquiry, this is creating increasingly robust tests for the ideas. Transformational innovations will be strong enough to matter in realistic settings.

When a new subject comes under study, a variety of unconstrained settings are typically used to formulate the issues and generate preliminary insights. These might include lessons learned reported from the field, brainstorming sessions, subject matter expert elicitation efforts, review of existing relevant research and experiments, and workshops designed to bring together experts from the relevant fields. These approaches have been widely used by the Joint Staff in developing concepts like *dominant maneuver* and *precision engagement*. They were also used by J-9, JFCOM in order to generate concepts such as Rapid Decisive Operations (RDO). While these activities can help explore a new topic, they are not experiments because they lack the essential empirical dimension.

Placing these ideas into a weakly structured experimentation environment, such as a war game, provides the opportunity to collect systematic data and capture relevant insights. While the free flow of ideas and the opportunity for a variety of behaviors makes these loose environments ideal for exploring a problem and generating hypotheses, their inability to be replicated and their low fidelity to real world situations limits their utility.

Experimentation campaigns should move the venue from these weakly structured settings into those with more specific and conscious controls intended to enrich the fidelity of the setting in which knowledge is gathered. This can be done by moving into the laboratory or moving into models and simulations. In some cases, both can be done at once.

Moving into a laboratory in order to work in a more realistic setting may appear counter-intuitive. The most widely understood purpose of laboratory settings is to control by screening out many real world factors. However, laboratory settings are also used to focus the experiment setting on factors believed to be important and ensure that their impact is assessed systematically. For example, war games intended to examine the effect of differential information on decisionmaking do not normally systematically control for the types of subjects making decisions or the decision styles employed, despite the fact that both of these factors are widely believed to be important. By going into a laboratory setting where factors like these can be brought under control through subject selection, research design, and statistical control procedures, an experimentation campaign can improve the match between the experiment and the real world settings where the findings will be employed.

Similarly, building a model or simulation is always, by definition, an abstraction from reality. How then, is the realism of the setting improved if these tools are brought into play to replace loosely structured war games? Again, the answer lies in the ability of the model or simulation to explicitly include factors believed to be important and to *exclude* the wide variety of issues not under analysis.

Note also that by using simulation-driven laboratory experiments, or human-in-the-loop techniques, both laboratory and modeling controls can be used to add realism and filter out extraneous factors. This is the primary approach used by J-9, JFCOM in their series of LOEs designed to develop and refine operational concepts, organizational structures, and work processes for JointTask Force headquarters in the future.

Laboratories and simulations are, however, *far less realistic* than the settings needed before a transformational innovation should be adopted. Exercises, whether command post (CPX) or field training exercises (FTX), represent the most realistic settings available for experimentation and should be employed in the later stages of experimentation campaigns. However, the realism available in exercises can also be, and has proven in the past to be, a trap for experimentation. Exercises are expensive and are typically used to train the forces involved. Even CPX are typically training events for commanders and their staffs. Training is about how the force does business today and will do business tomorrow in real crises or combat. However, transformational innovations often involve fundamentally different ways of doing business. These differences may range across all crucial elements – doctrine and associated tactics, techniques, and procedures; force structure and organization; training and preparation of leaders and staffs; the information systems used; and so forth. Hence, "piggybacking" transformational experimentation on exercises intended to train the current force is not a useful strategy.

Therefore, the ideal exercises for creating realistic experimentation settings will be those designed with the experimentation in mind. This has been done successfully, primarily when a narrow innovation was being brought into the nearly current force (for example, the U.S. Air Force taking training data about the impact of Link 16 and comparing with the performance of those without the innovation) and when the experiment was placed into a force created for that purpose (as in the Army's digitization experimentation and the Navy's series of Fleet Battle Experiments). At this writing, joint experimentation has been hampered by the lack of these realistic exercises. ACTDs are an effort in this direction. They represent demonstration experiments and are supposed to include mature technologies, but they have not always been transformational. They have tended to focus on technologies without the supporting mission capability packages that transformation will require.

Complexity of the Issues Addressed

This dimension of experimentation campaigns is itself multidimensional. A variety of different factors can impact the complexity of any one experiment and must, therefore, be considered when campaigns are designed. They are limited only by the richness of the knowledge domain under study and the imagination of the experimentation team. They include the:

- Number of subjects;
- Variety of actors (echelons, functions, and relationship to the U.S.);
- Stability of the operating environment;
- Linkage patterns;
- Information flows;
- Quality of the information;
- Degree of uncertainty; and
- Many other factors.

The key here is to recognize that complexity exacts a major price in experimentation. Campaigns typically begin simply, but cannot end there. Over time and across different experiments, more and more factors will need to be considered or examined and ruled out because they do not have measurable impacts. At the same time, allowing too many factors into a given experiment will make it very difficult to sort out the cause and effect relationships being observed. Very large designs, typically implying large expenditures, are required to deal with a variety of complex factors in the same experiment. Moreover, the tools to measure the impact of a variety of different factors, and keep them distinct enough to analyze them, will be a challenge in many experimentation campaigns.

Designing Experimentation Campaigns

While the cube shown in Figure 4-2 shows an experimentation campaign vector that starts at the origin for all three dimensions, not all experimentation campaigns for transformation will begin at the origin on all dimensions. The key to selecting the starting point is understanding what is already known and what experimentation has already been done.

In studying a new field with little existing knowledge, it is essential to begin at the beginning. Thecampaign will have to be organized around simple discovery experiments in weakly structured settings that mature over time as the domain becomes understood.

For examining an issue that has arisen from real world, military lessons learned and experience, the experimentation campaign may start in the center of the experimentation campaign space. Hypothesis testing in laboratory and simulation settings can be used to rapidly assess the robustness of the concept and refine its applications, as well as to isolate and identify areas requiring further research.

Application of a well-understood knowledge arena to the DoD may start even further along, in the region where hypothesis refinement experiments are conducted in relatively high fidelity, complex environments. These situations can begin to move toward demonstration experiments as soon as the main effects in the experiments prove replicable.

As a practical matter, experimentation teams seeking transformational issues should be looking for relatively mature concepts or issues that have been developed in other fields. For example, the search for business practices that have proven successful in high stakes, dynamic arenas was a good idea when looking for advantages arising from the introduction of new information technologies. Similarly, the existing body of research into the dynamics at work after natural disasters has proven to be a rich source of insight on the crucial topic of designing effective organizations with minimal infrastructure for a diverse set of stakeholders.

The other practical imperative for experimentation campaigns is that *they must be planned far enough into the future to ensure that resources are available to support them*. Given the complexity of conducting any experiment, lead time is essential. Adding the complexity required to accumulate knowledge and mature a concept makes it essential that serious planning be done. This complexity also means that plans for campaigns of experiments cannot be immutable. Learning in early experiments often leads to changes in later ones. However, those changes can be well within the planning parameters originally established, provided the experiments are not scheduled too close together and a "lock step" mentality is avoided.

Conclusion

No single experiment will be adequate to support a transformation initiative. Hence, experimentation campaigns should be used to develop mature knowledge and move concepts along toward mission capability packages. These campaigns will change over time in terms of the knowledge they generate, in the realism of the settings in which they take place, and in their complexity.

CHAPTER 5

Anatomy of an Experiment

Merely knowing what an experiment is (and is not) does not make it possible to organize and conduct a successful experiment. This chapter takes a deeper look into the anatomy of an experiment: the structures, processes, procedures, and products needed to make an experiment a success. This is an end-to-end review of an experiment, from its formulation to the delivery of its products.

Phases of an Experiment

Figure 5-1 shows an overview of the three major phases in any experiment: pre-experiment, conduct of the experiment, and post-experiment. The outputs of the pre-experiment phase provide "what we know" and "what we think" as expressed in the experiment model and experiment propositions in hypotheses, and "what we are going to do" as expressed in the detailed experiment plan. The output of the conduct phase is simply the empirical data generated by the experiment as well as other observations and lessons recorded. The output of the post-experiment phase is a revised model that captures and incorporates what is learned, empirical data that

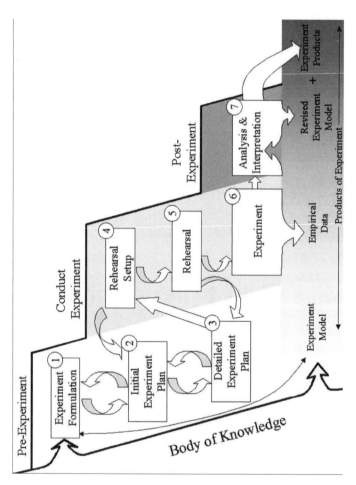

Figure 5-1. Phases of Experiments

others can use, the documentation of supporting experimentation activities, and other findings and conclusions such as lessons learned.

Unfortunately, there is a misconception that most of the effort required in successful experimentation occurs during the actual conduct of the experiment (the most visible part, when subjects are being put through their paces or the experimentation model or simulation is running). In fact, the bulk of the effort in successful experiments is invested before the experiment itself is conducted, in the pre-experiment phase. Moreover, substantial effort is also required after the experiment is conducted when the results are analyzed, understood, extrapolated, documented, and disseminated. This weak grasp of the required allocation of effort across the various elements of the experimentation process often creates mischief by mismatching resources against the work needed to produce quality results. Hence, this chapter looks at the whole process from the perspective of the experimentation team, identifies all of the critical steps, discusses their interrelationships, and asks what must be done in order to achieve success.

While the detailed discussion of each phase that follows is largely from the perspective of an hypothesis testing experiment, all of these steps are also needed in both discovery and demonstration experiments. Given the nature of DoD transformation, this discussion also emphasizes experiments involving human subjects. Also, given the formidable problem of exploring warfare in anything that approaches a realistic setting, a chapter discussing modeling experiments has also been included.

Pre-Experiment Phase

The objective of the pre-experiment phase is to define the experiment's objectives and to develop a plan for carrying out the experiment. Experiments, even if they are not explicitly part of a campaign, are not isolated events. There is, of course, an existing body of knowledge to draw upon, including the results of previous research and existing models that attempt to capture some or all of the behaviors and relationships of interest. There may also have been a number of related experiments, including some modeling experiments, to draw upon.

Well-run experiments will devote significant resources to *learning what is already known*. This can avoid blind alleys, save massive effort later, and allow the use of precious experimentation assets to move the state of knowledge forward rather than simply rediscover existing knowledge. While termed a *literature search* in academia, this effort involves much more in a realistic military context. First, it means knowing what relevant research (including experimentation, historical research, modeling, etc.) has been done and reported in published sources, including sources such as DTIC (Defense Technical Information Center). Second, it means an open source search on the Internet to see what research has been done, but is not carried in the formal journals or has not yet had time to reach them. Since Internet sources are not rated for reliability, this effort must be disciplined and accompanied by an analysis of the research and publication histories of the scholars, teams, and organizations responsible for each item. In addition, lessons learned documents, technical assessments, and other related materials should be gathered and reviewed. Finally, lead researchers who have worked similar topics should be contacted directly to learn about their current work and exploit their knowledge of the topic. Investment in this initial review of knowledge often pays high dividends.

Almost all experiments worth doing require a multidisciplinary team. Since efforts normally begin with only a part of the experimentation team in place, it is important that care is taken to bring the full range of expertise and experience needed to bear before settling upon an experimental concept and developing a plan of action. The types of experiments needed to develop transformational mission capability packages will, in all likelihood, focus at least in part on command concepts, information, cognitive issues, and organizational behavior. The reader is referred to the NATO *COBP for C2 Assessment* (Section 2-D)[1] for a point of departure on the building of an assessment team. That discussion includes the nature of the skills that are required.

The pre-experiment phase consists of four major activities:

- Formulating the experiment;
- Establishing the experimentation team;

- Generating the initial plan for the experiment; and

- Drafting the detailed plan for the experiment.

Formulation of the Experiment

Effective formulation is fundamental to the success of all experiments, but particularly in transformational experiments because the issues are complex and inherently involve the many dimensions that form a mission capability package. Proper attention to formulation will provide a solid foundation upon which the experiment can be built.

A review of the existing body of knowledge and previous experiments will provide the team with a good idea of what is known and what conjectures have some apparent merit. The first task in formulation is to properly understand the issues that the experiment will address and the context in which the issues will be addressed. This task involves the explicit definition of several items, including:

- Propositions, hypotheses, and/or relationships to be addressed;

- Assumptions that will be made;

- The identity of the dependent variable(s);

- The identity of the independent variables;

- Which of the independent variables will be controlled; and

• Constraints on the value of the variables for the purpose of the experiments.

Specific articulation of the problem is really what the experiment is all about. The assumptions made are another important part of the formulation of an experiment. They determine the scope of the experiment and clearly identify areas that are not being investigated. Making explicit assumptions is very important in helping one and all to understand and evaluate the empirical data that will result from the experimentation and its interpretation. It is always good practice to clearly articulate all of the key assumptions made.

The independent variables are the inputs. Taken together, they frame the experiment space. They focus us on the relationships of interest. The dependent variables are the outputs or products of an individual, team, or organization. They represent the characteristics and behaviors that are important to the success of military operations. The NCW value chain[2] provides a hierarchy of measures, any of which might be the focus of a given experiment. Given the complexity of NCW-related issues and the military contexts in which they will be applied, many of the assumptions will serve to fix the values of some subset of their relationships to one another.

The heart of any experiment is in what we attempt to *control*. Control can be exercised in a number of ways. While the selection of variables to be controlled is part of the formulation of the experiment, *how* they are to be controlled is determined in detail when developing the experiment plan. The formulation task is completed with the specification of constraints that will be imposed on the variables. Some of these may be a reflection of the assumptions; others are a reflection of the scope of the experiment, or as a result of practical considerations.

There are two major outputs of formulation. First is the construction of an experimentation model that contains the key variables and the relationships (some known, some hypothesized, some the subject of discovery) between them. Second is the specification of the relationships of primary interest, the related assumptions, and constraints.

Formulating Discovery Experiments

Discovery experiments, however unstructured they appear to be, are no exception to the need for careful formulation. They need to be designed around clearly articulated questions. For example, "what makes for effective collaboration?" is too vague. A more articulate question would be "how do differences in group structure, communications patterns, work processes, participant intelligence, participant cooperative experiences, and participant expertise affect the quality of collaboration?" The second version will make it much easier to design for success, including the crucial issues of what data need to be collected and how the data will be analyzed and exploited. When possible, the subject of a discovery experiment should also be stated in terms of the relevant environment or operating constraints that will bound the analysis. For example, determinants for quality collaboration may be sought at a particular level of command within a single Service, joint, or coalition context; or a specific part of the spectrum of conflict (peace operations, small scale contingencies, etc.); or using different types of participants (college students, retired military, active duty military, etc.). Failure to be explicit about these limiting conditions can lead to inappropriate conclusions about what is already known, what has been learned during the experiment, and what related research still needs to be undertaken.

Discovery experiments also require an open-ended articulation of the issue under study. While all experimentation teams should be alert to insights or research results that go beyond the specific issues under study, this is particularly important for those conducting discovery experiments. The fact that their purpose is exploratory makes it very unlikely that every factor that will make a difference will have been clearly articulated in advance. Hence, issue definition must be broad in order to ensure broad capture of what unfolds. This will also help to ensure open mindedness while the results are reviewed and interpreted.

Formulating Hypothesis Testing Experiments

For hypothesis testing experiments, the product of formulation needs to be expressed as a specific hypothesis or a set of related hypotheses. Unless simple "if...then...condition" statements can be articulated, the research issue cannot be converted into falsifiable propositions and the experiment results will not be clear. This includes the null hypotheses to be tested, the related-assumptions made, and the identification of the baseline condition for comparison. A good hypothesis differentiates between two or more treatments or sets of independent variables so that the results will be interesting and will advance our knowledge, regardless of the outcome. For example, the proposition that "information sharing will improve group situation awareness in combat" needs to be restated into a primary hypothesis:

> IF information sharing occurs, THEN group situation awareness will increase WHEN the subjects are military professionals working in a warfighting context.

It also needs to be understood to imply the falsifiable null hypothesis:

> IF information sharing occurs, THEN no increase in group situation awareness will be observed WHEN the subjects are military professionals working in a warfighting context.

Equally important, the research team will need to know how these propositions are anchored in the real world. That is, when the hypothesis is in fact testable by the experiment, then the experiment formulation will be complete. For example, the experimentation team will want an application context in which it makes sense that information sharing would increase situation awareness. They also want to ensure that the context selected for experimentation is one where improved situation awareness is believed to be valuable. They may also want to design the experiment so they can also test hypotheses about the importance of that shared awareness. The ideal experimentation context would have no prior information sharing. However, such conditions are very rare today. Hence, the research team will need to know how much occurs today and know how the experiment conditions will ensure that more sharing occurs on certain topics expected to increase situation awareness. The team also needs to have an understanding of what constitutes situation awareness and how more of it could be recognized and measured.

Formulating Demonstration Experiments

Demonstration experiments will normally have quite specific issues – they are set up to show that specific approaches and/or federations of systems provide military utility (effectiveness, efficiency, speed of process) in selected situations or operating environments. These goals can normally be stated as fairly rigorous hypotheses and sets of interrelated hypotheses. However, even these "simple" demonstration experiments should be set up to identify novel insights. Any time we task military professionals to operate in new ways or use new technologies we stand a very real chance that they will innovate or identify new challenges and opportunities. Ignoring that likelihood means a very real chance of missing the opportunity to gain valuable knowledge.

Articulating the Initial Experiment Model

One good test of whether the experiment has been formulated well is to circulate the underlying conceptual model. This representation should show the dependent variables, independent variables, the relationships between them, and the limiting conditions (context, assumptions, and factors to be controlled) perceived as relevant. This initial model is subject to revision and is unlikely to be stable, and will later form the basis for at least part of the analysis to be performed. If it cannot be articulated clearly, the experiment formulation is probably immature.

Establishing the Experimentation Team

As the research issue is clarified and the hypotheses are articulated, the research leader will be in a position to establish the experimentation team. Hopefully, this step is informed by early efforts to involve people with a variety of expertise. It may even be completed while the problem is being formulated. Experiments are rarely small efforts, so some help is going to be needed. Expertise will, for example, be required in each of the substantive areas identified in the issue and hypothesis articulation. This may mean military subject matter experts or operators familiar with the functions involved (information sharing and situation awareness in the example above), expertise in the academic topics involved (experiment design, data analysis, modeling), knowledge of scenario development, and technical expertise in generating and instrumenting a realistic experiment environment. At this stage, the core of the team needs to be brought on board, though others (e.g., observers and the bulk of the hands-on technicians needed to run the detailed scenarios) can be added later.

Initial Experimentation Plan

Following the formulation of the experiment, attention is focused on developing an initial experimentation plan. The process is iterative because a balance needs to be reached between what is desired and what is possible. On occasion, the formulation needs to be revised. Perhaps a variable that we wanted to control cannot be realistically controlled. Perhaps important new variables will emerge when the initial model of the problem is specified.

Two major activities need to be completed in order to develop the initial experimentation plan:

- Specify the initial research design including the development of the rough experimentation plan; and

- Simulate the experiment using the experimental model.

Initial Research Design

With the experiment formulated, existing knowledge explored, and a preliminary experiment model articulated, the experimentation team is in a position to take its first cut at the research design itself. This design contains several crucial ideas:

- What are the treatments of appropriate ranges of the independent variables and how will they be operationalized?

- How will each of the variables be measured?

- What factors are believed to influence the relationships between the independent variables, intervening variables, and the dependent variables and the interrelationships among the independent variables?

- How will control be established for those variables where it is needed?

- What baseline is being used? Is it pre-established or must it be built into the experiment?

- How much data (nature and number of observations) will be needed to generate clear findings and how will those data be generated?

- What analytic strategy is appropriate?

Each of these issues could be the subject of a major text in itself. However, the discussion that follows articulates some principles that can guide experimentation teams.

The Variables

This section discusses the nature of the variables associated with transformation experiments. They can be put into three groups: *dependent, independent*, and *intervening*. First, the dependent variables, which will form the objective function in the analysis that accompanies the experiment, must be chosen to ensure that they are valid and reliable indicators or measures of the anticipated benefits from the innovation being investigated. *Valid* means that the measures represent all of the concepts under study. This may well require multiple variables. For example, an innovation designed to improve decisionmaking may well mean that the decisions are both faster and more likely to be correct. Measuring only part of the concept, for example decision speed alone, would make the results of the experiment misleading. *Reliable* means that the measures selected are objective so that the same values will be recorded for the same observations. This can be a meaningful challenge when human behavior is to be recorded or human observers are employed. Thinking at this stage needs to extend to what will need to be observed and recorded and how that will be done. A more thorough discussion of dependent variables is included in the chapter dealing with measures of merit and data collection.

Second, the independent variables of interest must also be clearly articulated and the process by which they will be introduced into the experiment must be thought through. Moving from the concepts of interest in the initial model to the specific treatment to be introduced often proves challenging. This is particularly true when the richness of a true mission capability package must be introduced. While academic researchers will argue that experimenting with smaller elements will produce clearer findings, military innovation almost always involves a syndrome of factors. For example, analyzing a new technology requires analysis of (1) the work process shifts away from current practices to new doctrine crafted to exploit the technology, (2) changes in the organizational structures and information flows required to exploit the technology fully, and (3) alteration in the roles of those employing the technology. Hence, a mission capability package concept will normally form the basis of the treatments to be assessed. As with the independent variables, the experimentation team should try to avoid partial treatments that include only some elements of the mission capability package. For example changes that introduce a technology and supporting work process, but do not allow organizational changes believed necessary for them to be fully productive, will only show part of the potential impact from the innovation. They may even generate results that lead us in the wrong direction.

The initial experiment design does not require detailed articulation of the treatments. It does require understanding of how many there will be and what will be required to support them in the experiment. However, the development of detailed treatments can continue until it is time to integrate them into the federation of systems supporting the experiment and training those who will use them. The Command Post of the Future experiment on rapid visualization makes a good case in point. Their goal was to compare new presentation technologies with existing U.S. Army standard representations of a land warfare battlespace. In this stage of the process, the decision had been made to have two teams of researchers independently develop novel representations. Hence, the experimentation team could assume that the bundles of technologies and approaches (different use of shapes, colors, ways to represent movement and the passage of time, selection of different map backgrounds, etc.) would be organized into two treatments, each of which would represent a set of new ideas. A third treatment was the baseline representing the situation according to existing doctrine and practice. This was adequate for the initial experimentation plan. Indeed, several months would pass and a great deal of preliminary research would be done before the precise contents of the two innovative treatments were determined. However, knowing there were two innovations and a baseline was enough information to permit experiment planners to continue their work.

Identifying the intervening variables, those primarily of interest because they impact the relationship between the independent and dependent variables, must also be done with care. This is an area where prior research is particularly beneficial because it will help the team identify important factors and how they can be expected to influence the behaviors observed in the experiment. If these factors are not understood and identified before the experiment, they can be expected to have a major impact on the experiment's results and to confound the team's efforts to improve knowledge.

The most common intervening factor in DoD experiments has been the level of training. Again and again, reports have shown that an experiment failed to ensure that the subjects had adequate training on the new technology being introduced and therefore the experiment's results were dominated by the learning curve of the subjects. This means, of course, that the full benefits from the innovation were not achieved and its full potential could not be assessed in the experiment. In many cases, the weak training occurred because of a failure to cut off development of the new technology in time to create high quality training programs. The lack of a "good idea cut-off date" has been cited in numerous post-experiment reports over the last decade as a source of problems because the technologies were not ready when needed and the subjects had inadequate time to train on them. In other cases, the problem has been too little time allocated to the training process. All too often, training is shoehorned into a fixed schedule rather than given the importance and time it deserves. The exit criteria from training should be some level of proficiency, not a fixed number of hours of training. Thus, experimentation teams need to conduct performance-based testing on the subjects so that all the participants have at least a minimal capability before the experiment starts. The experimentation team can then use statistical controls to analyze the results in ways that factor skill level out of the analysis.

A number of other factors can intervene in many military experiments and will often need attention. A partial list includes:

- Reliability of the systems being tested and the infrastructure underlying the experiment;

- The intelligence quotients (IQ) of the subjects;

- The experience of the subjects;

- Experience of the subjects working together;

- Physical limitations of the participants relevant to the research (color blindness for presentation technologies, distances from individuals to screens they are responsible for monitoring, etc.); and

- Learning by the subjects during the experiment.

Note that many of these deal with the natural variety of the human beings involved. This implies that testing of participants and research into their backgrounds can be used to ensure that they are assigned to treatments so that their individual differences are not a confounding factor. In large experiments, this is normally done by random assignment of subjects. At a minimum, the potential intervening variables need to be measured so that their impact can be factored out in the analysis. In a simple example, experimentation with a new collaboration tool may involve communication equipment or software that fails during part of the experiment. The experimentation team needs to anticipate the need to record downtime, to identify the workstations impacted, and to isolate data that may have been impacted so as not to skew the analysis. Similarly, if, despite random assignment, one team in a collaboration experiment was found to be composed of individuals with significantly higher IQs than the others, then the experimenters need to be ready to use statistical analysis to control for that difference and ensure that it does not skew the results. At this stage, the key is to have identified the relevant sources of potential bias and developed a plan to (1) avoid them if possible, (2) test for them during the experiment, and (3) prevent them from impacting the results.

Baseline and Treatments

The initial research design also needs to be very clear about the manipulations and comparisons being made. Experiments are inherently comparative. DoD experiments are conducted in order to see (1) whether some improvements can be expected from some innovation or (2) which of two or more alternatives will yield the greatest benefit. Hence, it is often crucial to know how well the current practice performs. In other words, *some baseline is needed for comparison*. The baseline is sometimes available from prior work. For example, the rationale for the innovation may be lessons learned or requirements analyses that have documented current practice and found it insufficient. The process of time critical targeting, for example, has been documented as inadequate because it is too slow to strike many targets of interest to the United States. In cases like this, the baseline exists and change from it can become a very useful objective function. However, the experimentation team must also make sure that its experiment is realistic enough that a fair comparison can be made between the real world baseline and the experiment results.

For many innovations, however, no good baseline data exists at this stage. For example, the question of how many errors occur in situation awareness in Joint Task Force (JTF) operations is important, but documented only sporadically and in very different contexts. Hence, a research team seeking to experiment with tools and processes designed to minimize those errors would need to build a baseline condition (no innovation) into the design. Building it into the experiment plan ensures that data on situation awareness are collected in the same way and under comparable conditions so that valid and reliable comparisons can be made between treatments including innovations and the baseline condition.

Sample Size

The initial research plan also needs to take a first cut at the technical issues of how much data are needed and what will be the analytic strategy. These are rich topics and must ultimately be dealt with by having experimentation and analysis expertise on the team. However, a few rough guidelines can be offered.

First, experiments should be designed with the law of large numbers in mind. Most of the parametric statistics preferred for experimentation do not apply to sets of observations less than 30, though meaningful comparisons can be made between sets of 15, and non-parametric statistics can deal efficiently with as few as a handful of cases. Second, it is necessary to know what is being observed and to maximize the frequency with which it will occur and can be observed. For example, early efforts to experiment with alternative planning processes were hampered by the low frequency of plan production. However, by shifting the unit of analysis from the plan to the elements of the plan (missions, assets, schedules, boundaries, and contingencies), the research team multiplied the number of observations dramatically. At the same time, they also allowed the analysis to penetrate the problem more deeply by examining which parts of the plans tended to work better or worse under different scenarios and planning contexts.

The broad analytic strategy can usually be inferred from the preliminary model and the finite definitions of the variables to be observed and manipulated. If, for example, a discovery experiment is looking at how work processes and new technologies can be manipulated to increase speed of decisionmaking, the analytic strategy will be to compare the treatments while capturing the specific processes used and the way the technology is employed. This would imply difference of means tests that compare both the alternative treatments (combinations of work processes and technologies consciously built into the experiment) and those time periods during which novel work processes, structures, or methods of employing the technology were reported. The initial experimentation design would need to ensure a context in which dozens of decisions were made. If only a handful of decisions occur, the experiment results will not be rich enough to see patterns in the subjects' behavior.

If, by contrast, a hypothesis testing experiment were focused on the use of alternative collaboration technologies, holding work process and structure constant, the analytic strategy might well be to build an explanatory model that accounts for all the variation in the objective function. In this case, the treatment (alternative technology) would ideally be placed into a multivariate statistical package where the influence of intervening variables believed to be relevant could also be considered. This allows the experimentation team to test propositions about factors such as learning effects within the experiment and differences between subjects and build a richer model of the way collaboration can be employed in different contexts. Here again, however, dozens of relevant behaviors (collaboration sessions) will be needed to ensure rich results.

Rough Experimentation Plan

As the initial research design emerges for the experiment, the team will need to turn its attention to the plan necessary to carry it out. Plans, including experimentation plans, always involve five key elements:

- Missions - what is to be done;

- Assets - which organizations are responsible for each task; what resources do they have for them, and which other organizations will provide the support for each task;

- Schedules - when the tasks and subtasks are to be completed and how those efforts will flow over time;

- Boundaries - how the pieces of the effort are to be kept independent enough for successful implementation, but at the same time made into a coherent whole; and

- Contingencies - foreseeable circumstances under which missions, assets, schedules or boundaries will need to be changed.

As a practical matter, five specific items must be included in the detailed experimentation plan: the facilities to carry out the research design, the subjects, the scenarios to drive the experiment, the observation plan for data collection, and the experimentation schedule.

Finding the right facilities and fixing the dates for the experiment, including the rehearsal or pretest, are core issues. The nature of the experiment largely defines the facilities required. These include not only rooms or hangars in which to conduct the experiment trials, but also spaces for training and meeting with the team, meeting rooms for observers, spaces for equipment, spaces where visitors can be briefed without disrupting the experiment, and facilities to feed and house the participants. Facilities also include the computers and peripherals required and any specialized observation equipment necessary. Security is often an issue, not only for conducting the experiment, but also for the areas from which it must be supported. Most useful research and experimentation facilities are very busy at the time of this writing. Planning ahead will almost certainly require months of lead time and may well require a year or more. Facilities are both crucial and complex. A senior member of the experimentation team will normally be assigned to manage this effort and another person on the team will be given responsibility for detailed administrative support.

Subjects

Human subjects will be part of the experiment, unless it is a pure modeling experiment. They must be identified and arrangements must be made for their participation. This is a very difficult task, but a crucial one because the results of the experiment can only be applied with confidence to the population represented by the subjects. Here, again, a few guidelines can be offered.

Academic experiments typically rely on student populations for their subjects. They do this because they are normally trying to research fundamental human issues – how some stimuli are perceived, how individuals behave under different circumstances, how small groups function or change their work process under specific conditions, and so forth. When they want to understand the perceptions or behaviors of specialized populations (for example, older individuals, professionals who share some educational and work experiences, or those who belong to a working culture such as medical technicians) the academics must find pools of subjects representative of those populations.

DoD experimenters face precisely the same choices. In order to understand the behavior expected from military professionals, either individually or in groups and organizations, subjects *typical* of those populations must be used. To take a typical example, those concerned with the transformation of the military are interested in how novel tools and techniques will be employed 5 to 20 years into the future. Clearly, this cannot be done using college students unless the research focuses on very basic human perceptual issues (which colors and shapes are more easily perceived under conditions of distraction and time stress) or processes (how should work be allocated between humans and computers with a given level of information processing capability). If the problem involves military expertise, then the subjects must start with that expertise. At the same time, the use of retired personnel as surrogates, or even active duty senior personnel, will require that they be willing and able to accept retraining in order to get into the future *mindset* necessary for the experiment. Some clever researchers have even employed teams of junior personnel they believed would relate differently to their technical innovations than their senior counterparts. They are trading off a different attitude about systems and innovation against established expertise.

The introduction of different pools of subjects (as a way of controlling for some of the expected intervening variables) will, of course, impact the research design. Sufficient numbers of subjects of each relevant type and observations on their behaviors will be needed to test the hypothesis that the subject type did make a difference and more importantly, the null hypothesis that the subject type did not make a difference. The same knowledge can be gained by building different types of subjects into an experimentation campaign design by first conducting the experiment with one pool of subjects during one experiment, then trying to replicate the experiment using a different pool of subjects. This may be a useful strategy over time, testing propositions with different groups to see how broadly the innovation is useful. At this writing, DARPA's Future Combat System Command and Control Program, undertaken in close cooperation with the Army, has conducted an experiment with a flag officer supported by field grade officers and is planning to replicate it with company grade officers and cadets from West Point. Their goal is to understand how their innovations are employed by capable operators with different mixes of training and exposure to modern computing technologies.

Subjects also need to be *unbiased* in that they have no stake in the outcome of the experiment. For example, if the experiment is assessing the military utility of an innovation, people responsible for the success of that innovation are inappropriate subjects. Even if they make every effort to be unbiased, there is ample evidence that they will find that almost impossible. Moreover, using such "contaminated" personnel will raise questions about the experiment results. In demonstration experiments, of course, such advocates will often be at the core of those applying the innovation. In this situation, where the utility of the innovation has already been established, their extra motivation to ensure that the innovation is successfully implemented becomes an asset to the effort.

Subjects and teams of subjects also need to be equal in *capability* and *substantive knowledge*. In the event that some of the subjects have richer knowledge of the substance or processes involved in the experiment, that difference should be fed back into the experiment design. The design can sometimes be adjusted so that the bias does not impact the treatments in an unbalanced way (for example, the experienced subjects can be assigned so they are equally involved in all treatments, so their impact will "wash out" across applications). In any case, the fact of a difference in expertise or experience can be recorded and included in the data analysis plan to ensure a statistical test is run to detect any impact, measure its influence on the results, and provide a correction that will prevent misunderstanding or misinterpretation of the results.

Subjects need to be properly motivated. While academic researchers are typically careful to carry out double-blind experiments so that the subjects are not aware of the true research issues until after their participation, this is seldom possible with DoD experiments. Academic experiments also use a variety of incentives to ensure motivation such as grades for participation and monetary rewards for success are the most common incentives. These are not possible in most DoD settings. For example, the justification needed to capture the time of military and DoD civilians to participate in experiments requires a clear statement of the objectives. Moreover, unless they are given reason to believe that their efforts are contributing to significant efforts, adult professionals of all types, including military personnel, will not be motivated to put forth the best possible effort. Hence, the general purpose of the experiment should be made clear to the subjects. Successful DoD transformation, while avoiding change that does not have military utility, is a widely shared goal and has been shown to provide strong motivation to active duty military personnel, DoD civilians, reserves, national guard personnel, and the contractors who support them. However, these messages must be made clear to the organizations that are asked to provide subjects for experimentation.

In addition, if professional subjects believe they are being evaluated, particularly in artificial contexts such as those needed for experimenting with future organizational and doctrinal concepts, they will be hesitant to be creative and energetic when participating in the effort. In essence, they will seek to avoid risk. Hence, the experimentation team needs to make it clear to subjects that they are not the subject of the experiment and that it is the innovation or mission capability package being assessed, not the performance of individuals or teams. This message must also be conveyed to organizations being asked to provide subjects. Otherwise they may be reluctant to provide subjects or convey a wrong impression about the purpose of the experiment.

Subjects must also be available for the *entire* time required. Very often, the type of people needed as subjects are very busy. The more skilled they are, the more demand there will be for their time. Hence, the experimentation team must make the minimum necessary demands on their time. At the same time, requesting insufficient preparation time for briefing, training, learning doctrine and techniques, and working in teams, as well as insufficient time to debrief them and gather insights and knowledge developed during their participation undermines the experiment. Failure to employ the subjects for adequate lengths of time will badly compromise the experiment and may make it impossible to achieve its goals. This has been a very real problem in many DoD experiments. This has been particularly true when the experiments were designed for several spirals in order to create cumulative knowledge and train subjects over time in order to ensure the success of major experimentation venues such as JEFX and Millennium Challenge '02. Hence, the time commitment required for success must be fulfilled and the importance of personnel stability when requesting support is very high.

Where are subjects likely to be found? Experience suggests several answers.

- Some service organizations designate particular units to support particular experiments, while others identify particular organizations for experimentation over time.

- Some (i.e., JFCOM) are creating specialized surrogate organizations populated with retired military personnel or some mix of active duty and retired personnel.

- Some experiments are conducted as part of regular training exercises, either CPX or FTX. As discussed in Chapter 13, this "piggybacking" can be difficult as there is often tension between the training objectives and the experiment objectives.

- Pools of casual officers awaiting assignment or arriving early for military schools can sometimes be employed.

Efforts to introduce new technologies, not only JWIPs and ACTDs, but also CINC and Service experimentation may provide opportunities to experiment with mission capability packages.

Military schools can sometimes be persuaded to build relevant experiments into their curriculum. The Naval Postgraduate School has been particularly successful at this and the War Colleges can provide highly qualified pools of subjects. However, direct linkage to educational goals and incorporation into the curriculum are usually necessary for military school participation. This typically means long lead times for planning.

Reserve and National Guard units can provide subjects for experiments that are relevant to their missions. Again, some planning and lead time are typically necessary.

For issues that deal with human perception, the traditional sources such as college students and people attracted by advertising may be perfectly adequate.

Commands that have an interest in a particular experiment often must take the lead in making sure that enough subjects with appropriate backgrounds can be made available to ensure successful experimentation. Experimentation teams need to include military personnel and/or retired military personnel who can help them identify appropriate sources of subjects and communicate the legitimate needs of the experimentation team to those organizations.

Scenarios

The choice of the scenarios or situations to be used in an experiment needs to begin as the rough experiment plan is developed. *The NATO Code of Best Practice for C2 Assessments* contains a detailed discussion of scenario selection and is recommended reading for those who need background on the subject. The key principles include:

- No single scenario will provide the breadth needed for a successful experiment.

- The model of the problem, with emphasis on the limiting conditions as well as the independent and dependent variables, should be the driver in scenario selection.

- Scenarios should be designed to exercise particular levels of command (tactical, operational, etc.) because the types of information and level of detail needed change with those levels. At the same time, at least three echelons of command (one above the experimentation focus and one below as well as the primary echelon under study) will need to be represented in the scenario to ensure adequate richness for validity and credibility.

- The experimentation team should seek to define the "interesting range" across which scenarios can be spaced to generate a sampling of the problem under study.

- Scenarios must be given enough depth to be credible to the subjects and to allow meaningful interpretation of the results.

- Ideal scenarios permit creativity. While scripting will be essential to establish the context for an experiment, free play by both sides will be necessary to achieve the levels of engagement needed by the participants and meaningful tests of propositions involving human perceptions, behaviors, and decisionmaking.

- Scenarios, particularly in-depth scenarios needed for testing rich concepts and innovations, are expensive and time consuming to create. Hence, reuse of scenarios will be wise, provided that it does not compromise the experimentation goals.

- While approved or accepted scenarios developed on the basis of current military guidance should be used when appropriate, they may not provide an adequate basis for assessing innovations designed for the longer term future.

Observation/Data Collection

The observation plan – how data will be collected during the experiment – should be initiated as part of the experiment plan. This involves thinking through all three classes of variables (independent, dependent, and intervening). The observation plan should emphasize automated collection mechanisms that are as unobtrusive as possible. A few principles should be emphasized:

- No single tool or technique is likely to generate all the data required for a successful experiment.

- Observation should be as unobtrusive as possible.

- Automated collection should be used whenever practical. For example, computer systems can report how they are used and track automated interactions.

- Human collectors will be needed when human perceptions, decisionmaking, or collaboration are used.

- If recording devises are used, the question of how their results will be employed cost effectively must be assessed.

- Survey instruments, whether applied to observer/ controllers, experiment subjects, senior mentors, or other subject matter experts should be cross-checked by real time observation and empirical data.

- Observations should be shielded from the participants and from visitors of others outside the experimentation team until they have been validated and analyzed.

The key issue in designing an observation plan is access. The experimentation team must understand the physical situation in which data must be collected and ensure that they can be collected. This means both physical access and also enough time to ensure that survey forms can be completed, interviews conducted, data recorded, and subjects debriefed properly.

Feasibility Review and Exploratory Modeling

With dates fixed for the actual conduct of the experiment and a better idea of what is going to be done, work can begin on the schedule and deconflicting of the activities of the experimentation team. Before committing itself to a detailed experimentation plan, the team should (1) be satisfied that the schedule is feasible, and (2) attempt to develop an executable model or simulation of the issue or problem under study. To review the schedule, a PERT chart can provide a sanity check with respect to the interdependencies among activities and resources allocation. This is both a check on the logic underlying the hypotheses of interest and also an opportunity to explore the research space and find the "interesting range" where the experiment should focus.

The logic check performed by building an executable model is essentially one that ensures that the abstract ideas expressed in the hypotheses can be integrated and expressed in a somewhat more concrete form. The tools for this kind of modeling will be simple, employing systems dynamics, influence networks, IDEF 0, colored petri nets, or similar logics. (See the NATO *Code of Best Practice for C2 Assessment* for a discussion of the types of models and tools that might be considered.) Even so, they will require translation of the hypotheses of interest into sets of related values and integration of the elements of the analysis into a coherent theory.

Once the basic concepts have been translated into an executable model or simulation, it can be run across the range of plausible values for each variable of interest to determine those values and combinations of values that are worth researching in detail. Often the extreme values for many variables are simply not interesting, or they make no difference. In some cases, "knees" in the curves will be found – regions where the rate of change in some variable is altered. These are obviously worthy of detailed exploration.

Detailed Experiment Plan

While the necessary modeling and simulation are occurring, the experimentation team needs to be developing the detailed plan for the experiment. This builds on the earlier work done when the facility was selected, but shifts from relatively abstract issues to the very concrete problem of how the experiment will actually be conducted. The activities, which include identifying the necessary infrastructure, thinking through the controls needed, and developing an integrated set of data collection and data analysis plans, are typically done in parallel because they interact in important ways.

Planning for the Experimentation Infrastructure

Typical infrastructure issues that arise include the number and variety of work stations for the subjects, controllers, and observers; the architecture(s) linking them; the equipment needed to automatically collect data (and other information required by the Observation Plan); the specific simulation(s) needed to drive the experiment and to capture what emerges from the subjects' actions; and the systems needed to support analysis of the results. The level of classification for the experiment must also be considered when these decisions are made. These infrastructure issues are treated as a bundle because *interoperability* is a key issue. Failure to link the elements of the experimentation infrastructure together will result in a "kluge" of systems that is inefficient, raising the cost of the experiment, and increasing the likelihood that the experiment will not be fully successful. A senior member of the experimentation team normally takes responsibility for this element of the plan and its execution.

Controlling the Controllables

Having recognized that significant intervening variables exist, the experimentation team must decide, as part of the detailed planning, how their influences will be controlled. Some factors can be handled directly by the experiment design. This is strongly preferable if the differences are at the nominal or ordinal level of measurement because these types of differences are often difficult to control statistically. If, for example, teams of subjects are drawn from several nations (nominal differences) or groups with different levels of expertise (typically ordinal differences), the research design should provide control for these factors by ensuring each type of group is proportionally represented in each treatment. Other factors, particularly those for which interval or ratio values are readily available, can be controlled statistically. For example, differences in scores on IQ tests are interval, while differences in years of relevant experience are ratio. Both types can be controlled statistically as long as the number of subjects is adequate. This solution is also available when the subjects have taken numerically scored tests for performance on the systems supporting the experiment or being evaluated. Some variation in outcome can be expected based on individual differences in aptitudes, skills, or performance, and research designs and experiment plans seldom allow perfectly equal distributions of subjects on these factors. However, the superiority of the control introduced through the design will minimize the chances of a confounded experiment and reduce difficulty in detecting and assessing interactive effects.

Controlling Exogenous Influences

Visitors, particularly senior visitors, must be understood as a potential source of bias in any experiment. Their interactions with experimentation subjects, or even their presence in the experimentation situation can be expected to distract the subjects and alter their work processes. Hence, a well-designed experiment will include provisions for hosting visitors and providing them with an opportunity to understand the experiment, but will prevent them from impacting the results. The one-way mirrors built into almost all commercial experimentation and focus group facilities are a recognition of the importance of non-interference. DoD experimentation needs to recognize this reality and make provision to avoid this type of bias. A good technique used in some cases is to videotape all or selected parts of an experimentation session and use the tape as a way of giving senior visitors a rich understanding of the experimentation process. Another is to invite visitors to act as subjects in trials like those being used. This is usually easy when individual subjects, rather than teams, are being used. However, it requires an experimentation workstation, drivers, and other support to make it realistic. Like all such uses of videotape, however, the privacy rights of the participants will need to be preserved and appropriate permissions obtained before this technique can be used.

Data Collection and Analysis Plan

The final key element of the detailed plan is the development of an integrated data collection and data analysis plan. Teams that produce these documents separately almost always find that they have problems in analysis and interpretation. A data collection plan includes all of the variables to be collected, all of the places they are to be collected, all of the means of collection, and all of the places that the data will be stored for processing. The most common errors here are failures to provide for component failures (substitute data collectors, spare equipment, etc.), failure to provide collectors with adequate access (terminals, headsets, security clearances), lack of communication equipment so they can gather data, consult regularly, and flag problems from their workspaces without the subjects overhearing them, and failures to provide adequate storage (including classified storage). The data collection plan is an excellent candidate for peer review because it is crucial and because it needs to be both complete and clear.

The data analysis plan includes whatever processing or data reduction are required to convert what has been collected into a form that can be analyzed in the ways desired and the plan of action for that analysis, as well as the interpretation of the results.

Indeed, while experimentation teams collect first and analyze later, they must reverse that thinking in order to ensure that collection fully and effectively supports analysis. Common errors include failure to recognize the time and effort necessary to organize raw data (data reduction, structuring of analytic files, etc.), failure to ensure that the qualitative and quantitative elements of the analysis are integrated and used to cross-check one another, and failure to ensure that the analysis looks for insights from the full range of participants (subjects, observers, senior mentors, white cell participants, etc.). The data analysis plan should also include preparations for the use of modeling and simulation to examine excursions from the original experiment, perform sensitivity analyses, and update and improve the model used to understand the problem. The data analysis plan is also an excellent candidate for peer review.

Conduct of the Experiment

The development of a detailed experiment plan is essential because of the complexity inherent in transformation experiments. However, just as no military plan ever fully survives contact with the enemy, so no plan for an experiment can ever be implemented without adjustment, refinement, and augmentation. In preparing for and conducting an experiment, three steps are essential:

- Experimentation environment set-up;

- Rehearsal, or pretest; and

- Execution of the experimentation plan.

Experimentation Environment Setup

An experiment requires an artificial environment. This includes all the elements of infrastructure identified in the experimentation plan including workstations for the subjects; simulations or other drivers for the scenarios; communications linkages among the subjects, controllers, observers, and technicians supporting the experiment; databases; and logistics. This is a major effort, particularly for the technical support personnel. It takes time, often far more than originally estimated, to set the equipment up and check it out. Often the individual systems work properly, but they have problems working together, exchanging information, or accessing the same data. Integration of even well-tested and reliable system components is a formidable undertaking. Hence, appropriate lead time is needed to ensure that all the systems needed are up, interacting properly, and ready to support the experiment. This cannot be done effectively at the last moment. Problems that are experienced with the functionality or the availability of the systems impacts the subjects and the nature of the data collected. Thus, given that the proper functioning of the systems is critical to the success of an experiment, adequate attention, time, and resources need to be allocated to this activity. Experience shows that, in the name of efficiency and as a false effort at economy, this step is sometimes left until the last minute. More than one experiment has been undermined because the team responsible for the facility tried to bring it together at the last minute and found they had glitches that prevented timely and sufficient training or initiation of the experiment trials.

In some cases, only a part of the experimentation setup has been made available for the pretest. For example, only a small subset of subject workstations has been used despite the fact that the conduct of the experiment called for a much larger number. The experimentation team must make every effort to ensure that the initial setup is designed and tested in ways that are challenging enough to ensure that the test is an adequate representation of the environment required for the experiment. Moreover, plans will be needed to complete and properly test the setup between the rehearsal and the conduct of the larger experiment.

Pretest or Rehearsal

Conducting a pretest in which all the myriad elements required for a successful experiment are brought together and made to operate successfully is an essential prerequisite for a quality experiment. In experimentation, the numerous hidden pitfalls merely prove that "the devil is in the details," however, proper planning and careful execution can overcome these dangers and produce great successes, leaving sponsors and stakeholders proclaiming that "God is in the details!"[3] Holding a rehearsal can be expected to improve every aspect of the experiment, from the supporting scenario through the data collection and subsequent analysis. Failure to hold one will almost inevitably mean that some aspects of the effort will need to be corrected on the fly, greatly decreasing the likelihood of success.

To be really useful, every aspect of the experiment should be pretested. All the technical systems to be used should be brought online – simulation drivers; workstations for subjects, observers, and controllers; the full package of instrumentation; the experimentation treatments; communications devices; as well as the computers where data will be captured and stored.

The pretest should be scheduled at least a month before the experiment itself in order to allow time to diagnose the sources of problems, develop effective solutions, implement them, and conduct limited tests to make sure that the problems have been resolved.

Training

Subjects, observers, controllers, and other participants need to be trained for the pretest. Training should precisely address the skills to be used in the experiment. Moreover, the subjects being trained should be comparable to those who will participate in the experiment. Full trials should be run (though they may well lack the rigor of those to be made during the experiment) in order to enable dialogue between the members of the experimentation team, the subjects, and the technical personnel supporting the rehearsal. Observer training should also be rehearsed and data taken in order to ensure the training is successful and the observers have the tools and access they need for a successful effort. Training will also extend to the controllers of the white and red cells to ensure they can play their roles effectively and will not unduly impact the treatments under study.

Most of the results of the pretest will be obvious, but others may require some reflection and study. Time should be built into the schedule to provide an opportunity to reflect on the results of the pretest and to take corrective action. Because elements of an experiment are heavily interconnected, changes needed in one area will often impact or depend upon changes in other aspects of the experiment. For example, learning that the subjects need more training on the systems they will use must have an impact on the training schedule and may require development of an improved human-computer interface as well as new training material.

Each opportunity to improve the experiment should be fed back into the detailed experiment plan, both to ensure that the new knowledge is exploited and to ensure that its impact on other aspects of the plan are recognized. The detailed experiment plan remains an open document, changing in order to meet new challenges, but also providing a stable overall structure around which the aspects of the experiment are organized.

Execution of the Experiment

At this point the reader should certainly recognize that a lot of effort and thought will have to be put into getting ready for successful execution and may recognize the crucial role of those efforts in successful experimentation. However, all that hard work and careful thought can also be wasted if the actual conduct of the experiment is not carried out diligently.

Training of all participants is the last opportunity to identify and fix problems. It should begin with training the support team that operates the systems and who will need to respond if there is a problem as well as capture data about the problem. They will often train some of the observers, controllers, or subjects on the use of technical systems, so this "train the trainer" activity is very important.

As with the pretest, observers and controllers also need to be trained. While they have different roles, the actions they take during an experiment are often interdependent, so they should spend at least some of their training time together. This should include discussions of the objectives of the experiment and how they will need to work together to preserve its integrity. Training also needs to include a clear understanding of expected roles and behaviors so they do not bias or impact the results of the experiment, as well as ensuring that they can operate those systems that they will depend upon during the experiment.

Observer training cannot be accomplished effectively in the abstract. Data collectors need to collect data and be critiqued so their efforts will be productive. Realistic practical exercises and reliability testing are necessary. Often, part of the observer training can be combined with the familiarization training for subjects and should be a hands-on opportunity to actually collect data under supervision. This practice also allows the subjects to become familiar with data collection processes and to raise any questions or concerns they may have before the experiment trials begin.

As noted earlier, subject training is particularly important and has proven to be a major problem area in a number of past DoD experiments. Training must cover an understanding of the purpose of the experiment, substantive issues regarding the background or scenario, the processes the subjects will use to perform their roles, their roles in providing data, as well as the technical skills necessary to perform their roles. To preserve the integrity of the experiment, subjects should be able to pass proficiency tests before the trials begin. Given the relatively small numbers of subjects, subjects that are not properly equipped to perform their assigned tasks create significant problems later during the analysis phase. When this type of subject screening is not practical, scores on those tests can be used as a basis for statistical controls that either mitigate or hopefully prevent differences in proficiency from biasing experimentation results. Training is also a final opportunity to ensure that the subjects are highly motivated. Obtaining subjects who are properly motivated is achieved initially by subject selection, but all adults are capable of "turning off" if they believe the activity they are in is not serious or does not serve a serious purpose. Hence, sessions that include both motivation and opportunities to ask questions and provide feedback are very important during training.

The imminent prospect of an experiment tends to concentrate the mind and bring all the actors, including senior visitors, to the center of the stage. The actual conduct of the experiment is almost an anticlimax when it finally occurs. In theory, this conduct of the experiment harvests all of the prior work and thought and will, hopefully, proceed smoothly. At this point, the major tasks of the experimentation team are:

- Quality control – ensuring that the experiment that takes place is the one that was planned and designed, with no outside factors intruding in ways that undercut the purposes of the effort;

- Data integrity – ensuring that the right data are collected, that no biases are introduced by the collection, aggregation, storage or data reduction efforts; and

- Debriefing of all the participants to ensure that qualitative data are collected, issues that might impact the data or its interpretation are fully understood, and the insights available from everyone (subjects, observers, controllers, and the support team) are captured while they are fresh.

In fact, however, conducting a successful experiment often requires *practical and intellectual agility*. Things frequently go wrong. Systems break down, whether they are computer systems, reproduction systems, communication systems, or anything else. People who appeared to have mastered skills or sets of information during training flounder when they are asked to apply them. Participants become ill or unavailable because of family concerns or military duty imperatives. Schedules prove unrealistic. Senior visitors appear unexpectedly and must be made welcome and given quality information without impacting the experiment. The list goes on and on. In fact, if it were not for all of the effort and thought applied in developing the detailed experiment plan and conducting the pretest, problems would simply overwhelm the experiment team and cripple the experiment. Proper contingency planning makes it possible to deal with problems as they arise.

Each and every one of the problems encountered will need to be recorded clearly and thoroughly, so that the impact upon the experiment can be tested, and dealt with effectively to achieve a successful experiment.

Many of the common problems should have been dealt with during the pre-experiment phase when the experiment plan was developed. Robust and redundant systems should have been selected. Refresher training should have been built into the schedule. Reserve talent should have been built into the observer, controller, and support teams. Extra subjects should also have been recruited and trained along with the main group. Finding useful roles for these individuals, if they are not needed in the main design, is often a test of the creativity of the experimentation team. Plans for handling senior visitors should be in place. In summary, single points of failure should be eliminated.

However, Murphy's Law, that "whatever can go wrong, will go wrong," applies frequently to experiments of all types. Foreseeing and planning for every problem that may occur is simply not possible or practical. The last defense is the determination, ingenuity, and hard work of the experimentation team. Leadership must encourage an attitude that identifies potential problems honestly and privately (so their potential impact does not unnecessarily impact other parts of the experiment). Issues must be examined promptly when they arise. Best available responses and solutions, which may be simply tracking the time periods, subjects, or treatments impacted for later analysis, must be identified and understood by the entire experimentation team.

The raw data collected during an experiment are seldom in exactly the form needed for analysis. In a sense, the data need to be converted into useful information by being placed in the proper contexts. For example, observer journals may need to be converted into specific data points about topics of interest through a process of selecting relevant events and coding them according to definitions and coding rules developed before the experiment. Similarly, raw data recorded automatically about the use of systems will need to be aggregated by time period, topic, type of user, or other significant control variables. These data reduction processes should be completed immediately after the experimentation trials. Indeed, they can sometimes be initiated while the experiment itself is still underway. However, their quality often depends on having the team that conducted the experiment available to ensure resolution of ambiguities and understanding of the circumstances surrounding the data. Failure to complete data reduction on the spot using the full experimentation team has, in the past, limited the data and information available for analysis and therefore *reduced the quality of the experiments*.

Inexperienced experimenters often assume that archiving is only a last minute activity and can be postponed until after analysis is complete. This is a naive perspective. The raw material generated during the experiment may be lost when the supporting infrastructure is dismantled or reconfigured to support other efforts. Experienced researchers also know that the very process of analyzing data can change it. Moreover, database manipulation errors are common during analysis.

Finally, other research teams, with different data mining tools and analytic purposes may later find the initial data useful. Hence, archiving both the raw data and the information created in data reduction should be seen as an essential part of the experiment itself. This is consistent with the DoD "post before using" policy to encourage information sharing or reuse of experimentation data. This is also an important way of ensuring the integrity of the experimentation data. Note that it covers all of the crucial artifacts of the experiment:

- Raw and processed data of all sorts, including background information collected on subjects and survey forms completed during the experiment;

- Insights offered by experiment participants, particularly during debriefs;

- Lessons learned about the experiment and the experimentation process; and

- Experimentation materials (simulation drivers, interjections by the control team, briefings or other products developed by the subjects, training materials, databases generated during experiment play, etc.).

Post-Experiment Phase

Contrary to popular belief, the experiment is not over when the subjects go home and the VIPs leave armed with a "hot wash" briefing or later with the issuance of a "Quick Look" report. Several meaningful steps remain to be taken after the conduct of the experiment in order to ensure its success. These key tasks include:

- Data analysis;

- Integrating experimentation results from different sources and perspectives;

- Interpretation of the data and information gathered to generate knowledge;

- Circulation of draft results for comment and constructive criticism;

- Modeling and simulation to validate and expand findings;

- Revision of the products to incorporate the responses to the draft and the new knowledge generated by modeling and simulation;

- Archiving experimentation data and materials; and

- Circulating the final products.

All too often, "defeat is snatched from the jaws of victory" after an experiment because too little time and too few resources have been allocated to complete these tasks and exploit the empirical data that has been generated by turning them into contributions to the body of knowledge. One of the most common problems is the desire for instant results leading to a hot wash at the end of the conduct phase of an experiment, a quick look at the results a few weeks later, and a final report that is a shallow discussion of the findings reported in these early products. This excessive focus and attention given to early deliverables leads to an unhealthy concentration on the immediately measurable and anecdotal evidence. They are a legacy from training exercises where the purpose is prompt feedback in a well-understood problem set. This approval does not reflect an understanding of the complexity of experimentation. Hence, it undercuts the process of experimentation and reduces the impact of experimentation on research and development programs. This does not relieve experimentation teams of their obligations to plan experiments that generate results as promptly as is practical, but it does speak to the problem of post-experimentation efforts and the need to exploit experiments as much as possible.

Analysis

The most obvious effort of the post-experiment phase is analysis. This should be guided by the Analysis Plan developed as part of the detailed experiment plan. The nature of the tools and processes involved are discussed in detail inChapter 9. However, a few guiding principles should be noted here.

First, the ideal analysis plan involves a set of analyses, not a single analysis. This is a reflection of the fact that a variety of different data (subject background, skill proficiency, behavioral data, survey information, insights from debriefings, etc.) must be analyzed, but also a recognition that different analytical tools may be appropriate in order to understand the experiment results richly. The experimentation team needs to think about the "so what?" of an analysis to make sure that it is necessary and properly conceived. That is, they need to reflect upon the results of the analysis and the explanation of the results. Would it make sense? Would it be credible? Would the analysis, as envisioned, support the purpose of the experiment?

Second, the appropriate set of analyses will vary with the purpose and focus of the experiment. Discovery experiments will require open-ended tools and techniques that allow the analysts to explore weakly structured problems and unearth patterns they might not have initially anticipated. Hypothesis testing experiments will require rigorous tools and techniques that permit specific inferences and allow for statistical control of intervening variables. These should also be supported by approaches that allow for discovery of unanticipated patterns and exploration of ideas emerging as insights. Demonstration experiments, on the other hand, should be primarily supported by analyses that confirm their underlying postulates. However, even these experiments should not be reduced to mechanical calculations that fail to look for new insights, new limiting conditions, or novel patterns.

Third, analyses, like experiments, should avoid *single points of failure*. Each analyst or analytical team should be required to show their results and explain them at internal team meetings. Key findings should be deliberately replicated, preferably by an analyst who did not perform the first run. Tests for statistical bias and technical errors should be used (for example, the impact of outlying cases or other distribution problems, the presence of multicolinearity, or the absence of homoscedasticity) to ensure that the results are not an artifact of the analytical processes chosen.

Finally, items of interest from the experiment outside the analysis plan, such as insights coming from participants or anomalies arising from equipment failures, should not be ignored. Senior analysts should work to develop specific approaches, tools, or techniques that allow unanticipated issues and evidence to be understood and exploited to enrich the results. The NATO *Code of Best Practice for C2 Assessment* includes a rich discussion of analytic tools and models. It is recommended reading for those interested in greater detail.

Integrating Experimentation Results

The analysis plan will be composed of a variety of threads or independent sets of analyses designed to generate knowledge arising from different elements of the experiment. Sometimes these will be directly comparable or tightly coupled, as in the statistical efforts to measure direct effects and those designed to assess the impact of intervening or exogenous variables. Others will be qualitatively different, such as the results from surveys, structured debriefings, and behavioral observations. However, only a single experiment actually occurred. Hence, these different perspectives need to be integrated and used to cross-check one another so that the experiment is richly understood. Failure to integrate the data and information arising from the variety of analytic perspectives employed will lead to a weak understanding of the experiment and may well leave *unresolved issues or inconsistencies* in the analytic results.

Interpretation of the Results

Data and information, even after analyses, do not speak for themselves. They must be placed in context before they can be understood. The simplest example is that analytic results fit into larger frameworks. At a fundamental level, they are consistent with, contradict, or help to clarify prior knowledge and research. They may also clarify other experiments in a campaign undertaken to understand issues larger than those explicitly explored or assessed during the individual experiment. They may also address problems, issues, or decisions that are important to their sponsors and customers.

Effective reporting of experiments should discriminate between the findings and the interpretation of the findings. In a well-run, successful experiment the findings should never be at issue. However, interpretations of these findings will often be an important issue on which knowledgeable practitioners and researchers may differ. This is particularly likely when the research results are linked to important issues or support policy decisions that may involve a very different calculus.

Circulation of Draft Results

Experimentation is a research activity. Its goal is a rich and comprehensive understanding of the phenomenon under study. All too often, however, experimentation teams and the organizations that task them act as though these are closely held insider activities that should not see the light of day until after they have been fully analyzed and interpreted. In the worst case, results that are inconsistent with sponsor philosophy or inconsistent with perceived organizational interests are not circulated at all. These practices are antithetical to everything we know about effective research and learning from experimentation. Hence experimentation results should *always[4] be circulated*, as early as possible, among those with related interests and knowledge. This includes peer reviewers chosen for their insights and knowledge, the participants in the experiment, other knowledgeable researchers, and practitioners.

This practice should not be understood to mean that experimentation teams should rush their work to broad publication. The results circulated should be mature and should include the original team's initial interpretations of the findings. They should also be marked "Draft" and should be circulated for the explicit purpose of soliciting constructive criticism and feedback, both on substance and presentation. This practice will help to create and maintain communities of interest on important issues.

Modeling and Simulation to Validate and Expand Findings

While the draft results are being circulated, the experimentation team should return to its executable model of the problem for two different purposes: sensitivity analyses and revision of the experiment model. Sensitivity analyses are primarily used to learn how robust and how stable the results of the experiment are in the context of those intervening or exogenous variables identified as important or to examine interactive effects when complex problems are being researched. Model revision efforts ask how the initial model might be changed or enriched in order to reflect the results of the experiment better. In either case, these activities are actually part of the overall analyses enabled by the experiment. They will often impact both the final products of the experiment and any related experimentation campaigns.

Revision of the Products

Feedback on the draft results, modeling and simulation efforts, as well as reflection and discussion within the experimentation team will come together to support revision of the products. This will typically include some type of annotated briefing intended for general audiences, a detailed technical report with the data and analyses attached intended for researchers, and an executive summary intended for decisionmakers and policy makers and those who expect to implement recommendations arising from the experiment (with references to the more detailed documentation). Keeping these products consistent as the revisions are made is an important, and sometimes challenging, task.

Archiving and Circulating Data and Products

Final completion of the experiment includes both selecting the best vehicles to circulate the results and also archiving the experiment's artifacts so they can be reviewed or used again. Both are important efforts.

Circulating the products can be done in a variety of forms such as traditional paper distribution, e-mail to selected individuals and organizations, posting on Web sites, offering papers at workshops, conferences, symposia, and publication in journals or books. The more significant the experiment, the more broadly the team should try to disseminate the products. This is true even where the experiment fails to confirm the hypotheses under study. Such findings are extremely important in advancing knowledge, even though they may be a disappointment to the experimentation team or its clients.

Archiving is also crucial. Lost data, information, and experiment support materials are very real impediments to progress. They deny other researchers most of the practical benefit from the experiment. They also prevent, or make very difficult, replication of results, one of the key elements in science. Finally, they result in increased costs for later related experiments. Hence, the material archived at the end of the experiment should be inventoried to ensure that it is all present, saved, and available for recall. In addition, analyses and modeling efforts undertaken to better understand the results, or as a result of feedback from the draft products, should also be archived and indexed for recall.

Modeling and Simulation in Support of Experiments

Models and simulations play important roles in an experiment. These usually computer-based tools are used to support experimentation with military subjects. Also, there are occasions when the empirical data collection that is an inherent part of traditional experiments can be replaced by models and simulations. That is when models and simulations are the generators of empirical data, or more accurately, simulated data. These activities are called model and simulation experiments.

The use of models or simulations to explore important issues has been a long tradition in the military in support of operational planning and other important analysis efforts. However, these efforts have not always been organized as experiments. In many cases, they have simply been efforts to explore interactions within a parameterized space. Most such models and simulations are deterministic and amount to an exploration of the consequences of selected sets of assumptions. Indeed, the application of these types of models is necessary to help identify the interesting design space for more extensive experimentation and for performing sensitivity analyses over the results of an experiment.

To be an experiment, the effort needs to address the issue of uncertainty with respect to the dependent variables of interest. Hence, the systematic application of very large, sometimes deterministic, combat models can be thought of as experiments, though they currently are seldom organized that way. Indeed, since the basic purpose of the design of such models is to build a credible representation of combat interactions, the interactions built into them are usually heavily constrained so that the outputs are understandable to the communities they serve. In a sense, therefore, these tools are used as a special type of demonstration experiment to show that the processes under study conform to the assumptions and expectations of their users.

Increasingly, however, models are being created that use simple rule sets to explore interesting interactions. Such models often employ agents and sets of simple rules to explore behaviors and interactions among agents seeking to discover emergent behaviors in complex, nonlinear systems. They can be quite sophisticated (involving fuzzy logic and other advanced tools) or relatively simple. Most of these applications can be understood as discovery experiments designed to learn about important classes of interactions. These models and simulations can be extended to hypothesis testing experiments, though only with considerable care are the nonlinear properties inherent in them will challenge both hypothesis formulation and interpretation of results. Nevertheless, they hold great promise, particularly because most of them are very fast running and can, therefore, be used to rapidly explore interesting analytical spaces. As computing power grows over time, this approach may become more useful and more common.

Figure 5-2 shows how modeling and simulation activities relate to each other within the context of transformational experimentation in the DoD:

- Pre-experiment research should explore existing models and simulations (and their prior applications), reports of experimentation results, and other documentation. These are key subjects of study during the knowledge review in order to formulate the experiment;

- Development of an initial conceptual model to support the experiment. This typically static representation idealizing all the relevant variables, the relationships between them, and the context of the experiment is produced during the experimentation formulation;

- During the conduct of the experiment, models and simulations are used either as (1) experimentation drivers and support tools (in "human in the loop" experiments) or as (2) the data generation engines (in model-based experiments). There are two stages to the process of applying models: one is to develop the simulation environment, including the population of data, necessary modeling, and accomplishing the necessary engineering to ensure a simulation environment functions as intended; the second is to conduct the experiment using the tools;

- After the experimentation data are generated, modeling and simulation are used for sensitivity analyses and other exploratory efforts; and

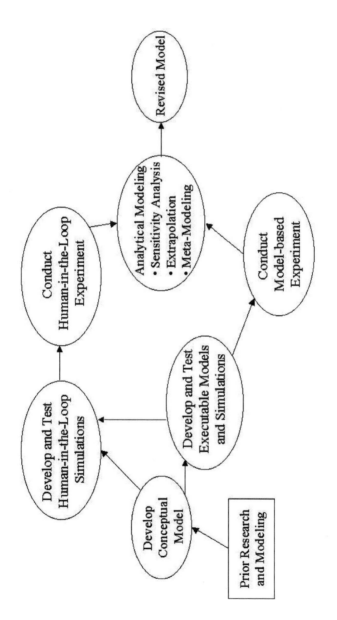

Figure 5-2. Modeling and Simulations

• A revised model is normally generated to capture the knowledge/results from the experiment.

There are a few important points to remember regarding the use of simulations, and other models, in support of experimentation. The first is that the application of these tools is not free, either in dollars or time. But, it is often a necessary investment to support any significant, well-crafted experiment. Significant investments in engineering training simulations, like the Joint Training Confederation, to represent new concepts should be preceded by the development of executable models. Reasonable investments in upfront analysis focused on the experiment can assist in focusing the larger-scale effort, ultimately making the effort more efficient.

There is a special case in experimentation called model-based experiments. In these types of experiment models, executable computer simulations substitute for human subjects for the purpose of generating experimentation data. All of the principles identified in this chapter hold for these types of experiments. There are also additional considerations, which are discussed in Chapter 12.

---

[1]The new NATO *COBP for C2 Assessment*.
[2]Alberts, et al. "The Network Centric Warfare Value Chain." *Understanding Information Age Warfare*. CCRP, 2001. p77.
[3]Ludwig Mies van der Rohe. *The New York Times*. August 19, 1969.

[4]*Always* is a strong word – but in this case the value of an experimental activity is directly related into the contributions it makes to the larger community – and even somewhat flawed experiments need to be properly documented and circulate so that others can learn from the experience.

CHAPTER 6

Experiment Formulation

Focus

This chapter and the ones that follow provide a more detailed focus on the specific activities that the experimentation team must execute. The keys to formulating a successful experiment are explored here from three different perspectives:

- Developing the propositions and hypotheses that will guide the rest of the experimentation design process;

- Creating and applying an initial model in order to define and explore the problem space under analysis; and

- Key experimentation design considerations, including both the essence of design and how designing DoD transformational experiments differs from designing "ideal" experiments from an academic perspective.

This chapter and the others that follow at this level of detail are also qualitatively different from those that have come before in that they use a single example, an experiment in self-synchronization, as a concrete case of each of the topics under discussion.

Propositions and Hypotheses

The topic of formulating the experiment, including making precise statements about the issues under analysis, was discussed earlier. The key points are (1) specifying the issues under study as precisely as is practical regardless of whether the experiment will focus on discovery, hypothesis testing, or demonstration of existing knowledge, (2) ensuring that the problem is formulated comparatively (including a baseline when possible), and (3) using background research of what is already known so that the statement of the problem includes all of the known factors.

Making Better Sets of Propositions and Hypotheses

A formal statement of the experimentation problem can be used to make the experiment more productive (greater knowledge gain for the same level of effort) if it is done thoughtfully. This formal statement should be termed *the propositions* when the experiment has a discovery focus because the level of knowledge is not yet mature enough to state the problem as formal hypotheses. For both hypothesis testing and demonstration experiments, the proper term is *hypotheses*. Note that both terms are plural. While it is possible to design an experiment that focuses on a single relationship between only two variables, *it is almost impossible to identify a nontrivial DoD transformation experiment problem that does not depend on controlling for some other factors or intervening variables.* Hence, the statement of the problem should be formulated so as to specify the whole issue under study, not just the specific hypotheses under detailed analysis. This practice improves the experimentation team's ability to identify all the elements of the problem and ensure proper controls are in place.

Another useful approach to describing the experiment problem is *selecting the propositions or hypotheses so that any possible outcome provides increased knowledge.* This is the logic underlying the principle that useful transformational experiments are comparative. This means that there are competing hypotheses. For example, the argument that standing JTF headquarters will enable "better" operational effectiveness implies that there are alternative bases for such headquarters (ad hoc assembly of tailored JTF headquarters, for example) that should also be considered and compared with the new concept under study. If such comparisons are made, then experimentation findings would provide important gains in knowledge if they established that:

- One or the other form is more effective, or

- Each is more effective under specific conditions (for example, ad hoc assembly is better for well-understood operating environments and missions that are primarily military; standing JTF headquarters are better for more novel environments and situations where a broad range of instruments of national power [economic, political, informational, and humanitarian as well as military] must be employed to achieve the desired effects), or

• Neither is more effective than the other in the experiment.

In other words, the propositions or hypotheses employed should be organized to create a win-win situation in terms of maturing the knowledge of the subject under study.

As noted earlier, all three basic types of experiment should also be organized so that the participants are alert to (and can provide) insights about factors not understood to be important during the problem formulation stage, but that emerge as significant during the experiment planning, rehearsal, modeling, conduct, or analysis.

Finally, *the actual statements of the propositions or hypotheses under study should take the form of an integrated set that specify all of the variables and relationships of interest and make it clear what will vary and what will be controlled.* This expression of the problem will be modified as the experimentation team works through the process, but it needs to be formulated as crisply as possible, early in the effort.

Propositions for an Exploratory Experiment in Self-Synchronization

Assuming an experimentation team was formed to examine the issue of how self-synchronization could be employed effectively in military operations, it would have to identify and organize the relevant propositions. Given the relatively weak knowledge today about self-synchronization, the team would conclude early in its efforts that this should be a discovery experiment. The team would have to assemble what has been written on the topic and would probably convene panels of subject matter experts from the military and also hold a workshop to bring together practitioners, experts from industry, and relevant academic specialists. That having been done, they might develop the following propositions:

- Effective self-synchronization requires high quality situation awareness.

- Effective self-synchronization requires a high degree of shared awareness.

- Effective self-synchronization requires congruent command intent across echelons, functions, and organizations.

- Effective self-synchronization requires high competence across all echelons, functions, and organizations.

- Effective self-synchronization requires a high degree of trust across command echelons, functions, and organizations.

- All five key factors (high-quality shared situation awareness, congruent command intent, competence, and trust) must be present for effective self-synchronization.

All of these propositions have the same dependent variable: effective self-synchronization. Four major causal factors have been specified, as has the need for all of them to be present. Hence, each is seen as a necessary yet insufficient condition. Note that a number of potentially intervening factors such as the leadership style of the commander, the possibility of cultural differences across coalition organizations, doctrine, and prior training have not been identified as specific independent variables of interest and may need to be (a) subsumed into the variables of interest (i.e., the team might try to include command style as part of trust), (b) inserted into the experiment (i.e., providing training and alternative doctrine to the participants), or (c) controlled during the experiment. Each of these potential intervening factors should be clearly articulated as an assumption.

Examining these propositions, the experimentation team should recognize that this is a huge experimentation space. Hence, in our example experiment, they decide to restrict the propositions under study to the U.S. and its very close allies

(UK, Canada, and Australia) and to crossing echelons and three key functions: information (including intelligence about the adversary and the operating environment); operations; and logistics, leaving self-synchronization across organizations (inter-agency, broader coalition, etc.) for later experimentation. In this way, the team has reduced the impact of culture by excluding all except the DoD and close coalition organizations. The temptation to reduce the problem further by excluding all coalition interactions was avoided because the experimentation team realizes that close coalition partners have been part of virtually every operation during the past decade and that self-synchronization is a crucial element in coalition efforts. They have narrowed the application range for the experiment to warfighting missions since other types would require interagency and broader coalition participation. These types of simplifying and clarifying decisions are crucial for success.

Initial Models and Their Use

First Descriptive Model

As the process of identifying and articulating the propositions or hypotheses underlying the experiment is being completed, the relevant information (independent, intervening, and dependent variables and the relationships between them) should be converted into an initial model. This model will draw from the existing knowledge being reviewed and will at first take the form of a static paper model in which variables are identified and the types of linkages between them specified. Creation of this initial, heuristic model is an excellent way to ensure that the experimentation team has thought the problem through precisely. Very often, ambiguities will be identified, new variables incorporated, competing propositions specified, and differences in emphasis will emerge as this model is developed and perfected. This initial model also becomes the mechanism for noting where assumptions will be made, which variables will be controlled, and which will be manipulated to answer the key issues under analysis. The result of this effort is a descriptive model of the experiment problem.

Descriptive Model of Self-Synchronization Example Experiment

The experimentation team building a simple descriptive model of self-synchronization would quickly realize that a number of factors would enter into the problem. Figure 6-1 illustrates how they might diagram these factors. Three factors were ultimately seen as direct causes of effective self-synchronization: high-quality shared situation awareness, congruent command intent, and trust. Two of the factors originally identified as direct causes were moved back a layer. Competence was perceived to be a causal factor of trust, but also to increase the likelihood of two other second level factors: congruent command intent, and empowering leadership. Common perceptual filters arising from shared knowledge and experience

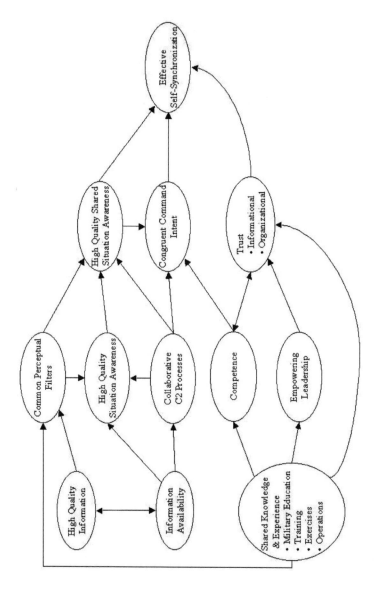

Figure 6-1. Illustrative Initial Descriptive Model: Self-Synchronization Experiment

were seen as key to both high-quality awareness and shared awareness. High-quality situation awareness was seen as a necessary ingredient for high-quality shared situation awareness, which also depends on collaborative command and control processes, information availability, and common perceptual filters. Empowering leadership was also specified as essential to trust, but it and collaborative command and control processes were not even explicitly recognized in the initial formulation. Finally, shared knowledge and experience were recognized as keys to trust, competence, and creating common perceptual filters.

Initial Executable Model

While the initial descriptive model is a very useful exercise, creation of an executable version will also help the experimentation team in important ways. This model is typically done in some very simple form using transparent tools. Systems dynamics models, influence diagrams, IDEF 0 models, ACCESS, and similar tools have proven useful because they are easy to use and because the relationships built into them are easy to understand.

Specifying an executable model will help the experimentation team because it forces them to think through the experimentation formulation in greater detail than is required in either the experiment formulation process (at the proposition or hypothesis level) or in creating the initial heuristic model. For example, specific input parameters must be given values and ranges. Assumptions need to be translated into parameters. The form of relationships between pairs or sets of variables must be translated from words into mathematical functions. In other words, greater precision and rigor are required.

The executable model, once developed, can also be used to focus the experiment. For example, by exercising this model across the range of plausible values for important independent variables, the experimentation team can narrow the focus of the experiment to the interesting range, the set of values that appear to make a meaningful difference in the dependent variables of interest.

Executable Model for the Self-Synchronization Experiment

It is difficult to show an executable model in a paper document. In this case the experimentation team would use a flexible tool, such as influence diagrams. This would have the advantage of forcing the team to specify operational definitions for each of the factors in the initial model, as well as the set of relationships believed relevant for the linkages in the model. Such an application, supported by prior research on related topics, would indicate several things important to the experiment. For example:

- Any value for trust that is not extremely high would prevent self-synchronization;

- Any value for competence that is not extremely high would prevent self-synchronization;

- Any value for quality of information that is not high would prevent achieving high-quality situation awareness, which would make high-quality shared situation awareness almost impossible; and

- Any value for system reliability that is not high will reduce trust and may lead to commanders being unwilling to empower their subordinates.

As a consequence of these model findings, the focus of the experiment should be narrowed and these factors should be controlled. This implies that the underlying quality of the information available during the experiment should be high, though that can include a clear understanding of what is not known and the uncertainty surrounding what is "known" or perceived. It also implies that the subject pool needs high competence in their roles – novices (alone or with experts) cannot be employed. Moreover, the teams of subjects must either be drawn from some existing organizations where trust already exists or put through a training phase during which trust is developed and validated before the experiment trials begin. Finally, the reliability of the supporting information systems will need to be controlled as a causal factor.

Ideal Versus Real Transformational Experimentation

Focus

The topic of experimentation design is complex and has been the subject of numerous textbooks. Moreover, the field changes constantly as progress is made in inferential statistics, the mathematics of nonlinear systems, and the computational power available to researchers. Hence, *the single most important consideration for those responsible for experimentation design, whether single experiments or campaigns, is to ensure that current expertise is available to support the plan.* Almost without exception, this will mean doctoral level (Ph.D.) training and a decade or more of experience in actually designing and conducting experiments. Moreover, most transformational experimentation will require experience and expertise in the social sciences because the human element is so crucial. This expertise is available from a few serving officers with such training, from the DoD and Service civilians in the research establishments, from federally funded research and development centers, from industry, and from academia.

This discussion, therefore, focuses on key concepts and principles that should be understood by all the members of experimentation teams, as well as by those who sponsor experimentation and must act on its results. The focus, then, is on understanding the logic underlying successful experiments and recognizing when that logic is being violated or may come into question. *Bad experiments, which cloak weak or false knowledge in an aura of science, will make mischief, not music.* At a minimum they will slow the process of understanding the impact of innovation on transformation (by forcing other research and experimentation to learn and demonstrate that they are wrong) and cost money (by encouraging investments that will not pay off as expected). At a maximum, bad experiments will lead to flawed mission capability packages that fail in the field. Hence, everyone involved has a serious quality control function to accomplish. This section is intended to help the experimentation team and their sponsors to perform that role. After this discussion of ideal experimentation, the Code looks at some of the imperfect circumstances and conditions faced by transformational experimentation efforts and how they can be overcome in the practical context of military analyses.

Ideal Experimentation

The hard sciences, like physics and chemistry, were the first to rely on experimentation in order to develop knowledge. The ideal experiment is one in which all the possible sources of variation are excluded except the one of interest. For example, to genuinely determine how fast objects fall requires creating a vacuum to exclude the effects of air density and wind. An experiment that measured the falling rates for ball bearings and bowling balls in the open air would conclude that the ball bearings fell more slowly because of the presence of air resistance and the differences in mass between the two objects. This experiment also requires a clear theory that identifies the causal factors (in this case mass) and limiting conditions (the vacuum). Moreover, a successful experiment also requires precise, correct, and reliable measurement of the active variables (mass, distance, and speed) as well as the limiting condition (presence of a vacuum or absence of air). Successful experimentation also requires an apparatus that measures speed precisely and allows the experimentation team to know exactly when the object starts to fall and exactly when it passes some other known point, as well as the distance between the start and finish. These two points also need to be far enough apart that the measurement instruments see enough difference to allow inferences about relative speed.

The goal of an experiment is always to advance knowledge. Because Western, rational science always allows for new insights and knowledge, nothing can ever be perfectly or permanently proven. Hence, null hypotheses are used to disprove false knowledge. In the ball bearing/ bowling ball experiment, the null hypothesis is that these objects will fall at different rates in a vacuum. The two types of objects are called the treatments, which means nothing more than that they are the ways that the independent variable is changed. The term *treatment* comes from medical experimentation where patients are given alternative medicines or procedures (including placebos, which serve as a baseline and allow for meaningful comparison) in order to determine the effectiveness of the different medications. Moreover, Western science is inherently skeptical, so experiments must be conducted a number of times and replicated using different subjects, kinds of treatments, methods of measurement, and apparatuses before their conclusions become accepted.

Later experiments can be used to move from this ideal knowledge to take into account factors that were initially excluded. For example, the shape of the object was controlled in the initial experiment, but would be important for objects falling through air. Those designing parachutes need to understand how manipulating mass and shape can alter the rate of descent. Similarly, those designing bombs or shells would need to understand the effects of wind. Therefore, the purpose of the research will help to determine the campaign of experimentation. Here again, a number of different trials will be needed. This is the functional equivalent of relaxing assumptions in a model in order to extend our understanding of the phenomenon under study.

Principles of Experimentation

This discussion should help to identify the basic principles underlying experimentation. Ideal experimentation manipulates only one independent variable at a time. Differences of this variable (the treatments) typically include some *baseline* (for example, the placebo in medical research) against which the effectiveness of other treatments can be measured.

Ideal experimentation observes change in *only one* dependent variable. This does not mean that only a single measure is used. If the dependent variable has more than one important dimension (for example, both the speed and quality of decisionmaking), all should be measured. Similarly, if the measures available are not totally valid (do not measure exactly and completely the concept of the dependent variable), multiple measures that provide relevant information about different aspects of the dependent variable (called indicators) may be taken.

Ideal experimentation excludes, or controls for, all relevant extraneous or intervening variables. If this is not done, then the changes in the dependent variable may be due to these factors and not to the treatment under study. While challenging in physical experiments, this becomes extremely difficult when dealing with human subjects, whether individuals or teams. When possible, every extraneous cause must be excluded. When this is not possible, the effects of extraneous variables should be manipulated so that they are "equal" across treatments and trials. For example, when large numbers of people are being used as individual subjects, they are typically assigned randomly to the trials. As a final resort, measurement is made on the possible intervening variables (for example, molecules of air per cubic foot in the vacuum, intelligence quotients for individual subjects, time spent working together for teams) and statistical procedures are used to estimate the relationship between the intervening variables and the outcomes across treatments.

This is possible for all kinds of measures, including nominal measures such as male/female that have no direction. However, it is time consuming, complex, and difficult to explain to those without scientific training (meaning it can have serious credibility problems), so statistical control should always be used as a last resort.

Ideal experimentation involves *valid*, *reliable*, *precise*, and *credible* measurement of all variables. If the experimentation team cannot perform proper measurement, the experiment cannot be successful. This cuts across all types of variables: independent, dependent, and intervening. *Valid measurement* means measuring exactly what you intend to measure and not some surrogate chosen because it is easier to measure. Some complex issues, like quality of collaboration, may have to be observed indirectly through indicators or by a set of measures, each reflecting some part of the concept. *Reliable* means that the same value will be recorded every time from the same event or activity. This requires particular attention when human behavior is measured or humans are used to perform the measurement. *Precise* means that the instruments are calibrated to fine enough tolerances to detect meaningful differences. It is really an extension of reliability. If the measures or measuring instruments being used are so imprecise that they cannot differentiate between substantively different values, the experiment cannot succeed. *Credible measurement* means that the system of measures is understood and respected by both the research community and the operational community that will be asked to act on the knowledge generated from the experiment.

Ideal experimentation includes enough data collection opportunities to support the inferences needed to translate findings into actionable knowledge. Something that happens once may be suggestive or illustrative, but it is not credible in a scientific sense. For an experiment to be successful, a number of independent observations are needed. *Independent* means that the observations are not causally related. For example, in most medical experiments, the number of individuals participating is the relevant number. Any factor in common across the individuals threatens the independence of the observations. The issue of how many independent trials are needed is a complex technical one that depends on (a) how many treatments are under study, (b) the number of intervening variables that are hypothesized to be relevant and must be controlled statistically, (c) the level of confidence that the experimentation team believes it needs to make meaningful statements, and (d) the population that the experimentation team intends to extend its findings to cover. This is a technical issue where statistical expertise is essential. However, identifying possible threats to the independence of the trials is a task for everyone involved in the experiment.

As a rule of thumb, the basic design for any experiment should attempt to involve at least 30 independent observations of any meaningful data category. For example, a three-treatment experiment involving two different types of subjects would ideally be designed around a three-by-two matrix with 30 people in each cell, or a total of 180 subjects (or observations), 90 of each type of subject. However, if each subject can be used for a single trial in each of the three treatments (thereby controlling for differences between individual subjects within each of the individual groups), the minimum number of subjects required declines to 60 (30 of each subject type). Prudent experimentation designers do not, however, plan for the minimum number of independent observations. Subjects tend to become ill or miss their appointments. Because most inferential statistics allow stronger inferences when the number of independent observations rises, over-designing the numbers needed in an experiment will both protect an experiment from potential shortfalls and also increase the likelihood of unambiguous findings. Of course, as the number of independent trials increases, the greater resources will be needed for a successful experiment.

A very different approach is often taken when working with teams of subjects or organizations. Employing large numbers of teams or organizations (such as command centers) for an experiment is difficult and may be impossible. In these cases, the groups of subjects should be selected so that they are as typical a population as possible. In these cases, the focus of the experiment design becomes the collection of enough independent observations of relevant behaviors to achieve the experimentation objectives. For example, efforts to determine the determinants of quality command and control early in the 1980s focused on decision cycles during military exercises. A 1-week Army division or Navy fleet experiment was found to generate about 50 major decisions, adequate to support treating them as experiments for purposes of testing hypotheses about the driving factors for effective command and control. Note that this approach makes it much easier to generate meaningful findings from a single experiment, but requires establishing how "typical" the exercise and the observed command centers are of all military decisionmaking. Hence, this work required an experimentation campaign as well as data on the relevant training and experience of the commanders and staffs involved in each exercise.

Note also that this approach also assumes that each event (decision, collaboration session, etc.) being counted as an observation is independent of the others (that is, not influenced by them). This is not always true. For example, high-quality decisions early in an experiment may mean that the team has a better grasp of the situation than others making weaker decisions and may also mean they are under less pressure during later decision cycles. Hence, the analysis plan for this type of experiment will need to include tests for the independence of observations over time and make provision for statistical analyses that control for this potential "contamination." Fortunately, these controls are available and used commonly in the social sciences, biology, and other fields where purely independent observations are hard to obtain.

Ideal experimentation generates *findings*, *interpretations*, and *insights*. *Findings* are the data generated during the experiment and the direct inferences available from those data. They take simple, descriptive form, such as "operational level command centers working familiar problems required an average of 3.5 hours (54 observations) to recognize and react to major changes in the battlespace, while working on unfamiliar problems required an average of 9.3 hours (49 observations) and this difference was statistically significant (p=.0001)."

Interpretations, on the other hand, involve conjectures, which often arise from prior research or experience. In this case, the experimentation team might report that the additional decision cycle time required in the unfamiliar situation appeared to occur because the command center appeared to take more time to gather information and to discuss what it meant. However, unless data were taken on the time and effort used to gather information and discuss what it means, this is not a finding. Indeed, humans have such a strong tendency to find an explanation for what they observe that they often draw wrong conclusions when not challenged to actually measure what occurs. Competing explanations are often offered for observed behaviors and can only be resolved by further experimentation or consulting research done by others that focuses on the alternative explanations. For example, another researcher might argue that the additional time taken was actually a function of the risk aversion of military command centers and a failure to recognize the urgency of novel developments in the unfamiliar contexts. Only a thorough research effort or a well-crafted experiment will allow resolution of differences in interpretation because the true data or findings typically support them equally.

Finally, *insights* are the new thoughts or patterns that emerge when the experimentation team looks at the findings or reviews them with outside experts, including the sponsors of the experiment. These may take the form of new hypotheses (cause and effect relationships), new limiting conditions (intervening variables), or even anomalies (data points or patterns that are inconsistent with the bulk of the evidence and our current theories and hypotheses). All of these are valuable, but the anomalies are the most important, because they may be clues to important new knowledge. Of course, they may also simply be anomalies – times when subjects behaved in unusual ways or low probability events that will not occur often enough to be worth attention. Because our level of knowledge about transformational innovations remains immature, every experiment is likely to identify important new insights. Failure to capture them will impede progress.

Peer review, *debate*, and *discussion* are the lifeblood of successful experimentation. While some DoD experiments involve classified information, many do not. In all cases, experimentation results should be circulated as widely as possible. Science and the ability to build actionable knowledge are accelerated by exposing ideas to review and holding healthy debates about what is known and what has been learned. This principle underlies the academic stress on publication in refereed journals – the editors act as a first line of defense against poor work, the reviewers who examine drafts are the second, and the general readership are a third.

The DoD does not need refereed journals, but it does need to tap the breadth and depth of available expertise in order to examine transformational innovations and the experiments performed to assess them and mature the concepts underlying them. Circulation of draft results among respected colleagues, briefing across a variety of audiences, presentations at professional meetings, and workshops to review and build on experiments and experimentation campaigns are all available to ensure peer review, debate, discussions, and alternative explanations. Each of these sources of constructive criticism and new insights, however, cost effort and time. These investments need to be built into plans for experimentation.

Transformational experimentation must seek *new knowledge*, not support for specific ideas. One of the attractive features of experimentation is the fact that not all the concepts or ideas put forward will prove useful. The DoD has a tradition of making everything a success wherein exercises cannot be failures because that would be a negative indication of organizational performance and readiness. Assessments of new systems cannot be failures because they represent major investments. Moreover, failed programs imply that those who developed them have not done their jobs well. However, experimentation, particularly successful experimentation, means finding out that some concepts or ideas are better than others, or more commonly, that two competing ideas or concepts are better than one another under different conditions (in different settings or for dealing with different problems). DoD experimentation needs to recognize this essential principle and not get trapped in a search for a single solution to all problems or a premature "shoot off" between competing concepts.

Transformational Experimentation Realities

Careful reading of the discussion of ideal experimentation clearly shows that this process is robust. Many of the processes and procedures that have emerged are designed precisely to enable knowledge gains under difficult circumstances. Robustness comes from anchoring the experiment in existing knowledge, using an open process that involves peer review, developing robust models of the phenomenon under study, and using tools and techniques that allow for cross-checking and questioning assumptions.

That having been said, *every experiment* should seek to conform as closely as possible to the ideal experimentation design. However, two major realities indicate that transformation experimentation will differ in two important ways:

- Transformation will not be accomplished by small, isolated changes. Transformational initiatives will always be rich combinations of mutually reinforcing changes, such as MCPs that cut across the DOTMLPF spectrum and go beyond it to include new ways of thinking about warfare and national policy effectiveness.

• The pace of change required for DoD transformation will not allow for a large number of sequential experiments designed to authoritatively explore every nook and cranny of possible alternatives.

Fortunately, these two realities and the pressures they generate can be managed successfully by thoughtful programs of experimentation and design of individual experiments.

At the conceptual level, transformational innovations (in this case, MCPs) need to be seen and organized as a *single, coherent, holistic phenomenon*, not as a patchwork of individual, separable initiatives. Indeed, many of the key changes involved in transformation will fail or have very little impact if undertaken in isolation. Business has discovered that adopting advanced information technologies without altering their fundamental ways of doing business (organizations, work processes, etc.) to take full advantage of the new technology means that only a fraction of the potential benefits actually occur. The same principle applies to military innovation and transformation. The elements of an MCP for transformational experimentation need to be thought of as a syndrome or an integrated, distinctive pattern of changes. Removing any one element means that the innovation is a different phenomenon, with different implications.

Hence, experimentation teams concerned with transformation need to develop full mission capability packages and treat them as coherent wholes when designing experiments. This means that they will logically form one change, innovation, or *treatment*. However, the metrics chosen and tracked, as well as the debriefings of subjects, observers, controllers, and experiment support personnel will need to be sensitive to the possibility that some components of the package are working better or worse than others, or even that some components are interfering with one another. Hence, the research design and analysis plan should call for analyses that help track performance of the elements of the innovation.

Besides treating the MCP as a single innovation, experimentation teams also need to rely heavily on the *research conducted by others*, both to focus their experiments and to help determine how much confidence to place in their results. Because MCPs will typically be composed of several different initiatives (changes in process, structure, etc.), several different research traditions will normally be available to help understand the phenomenon under study and to assist in the interpretation of the experiment findings. Moreover, because experimentation is conducted in a variety of different DoD organizations (Services, CINCs, and Agencies), work on analogous issues and problems will often be available to help understand what is being learned. Interaction and cross-talk between these efforts will provide important knowledge and accelerate the process of learning. Findings that are consistent with existing knowledge and other efforts at experimentation and research in analogous topics will allow rapid progress. On the other hand, inconsistent findings will be "red flags" indicating more thought, research, and experimentation are needed promptly on key issues.

Finally, the need to move ahead rapidly and to work in the large leaps implied by MCPs increases the crucial role of *circulating findings widely and subjecting them to vigorous review and rigorous debate*. The DoD has enormous analytical and operational talent available, both in the active force and in the organizations and institutions that support that force. While transformational experiments will challenge conventional wisdom and should not be expected to quickly build consensus within the naturally conservative military community, they can be expected to spark lively debate and serious discussion. Powerful ideas, the kind necessary for successful transformation, will develop strong empirical support from intelligent campaigns of experimentation. Understanding that evidence and its implications will require examination from a variety of perspectives.

CHAPTER 7

Measures and Metrics

Focus

Experiments are inherently empirical. Whether focused on discovery, hypothesis, or demonstration, experimenting must include capturing data and organizing it to provide the basis for analysis on the key issues under study. Hence, experiments always involve measurement. Deciding what to measure and how to measure it is a crucial step in any experiment. The old saying, "garbage in, garbage out" sums up the experimentation team metrics challenge. Unless good decisions are made in this arena, no amount of analysis or interpretation will generate a successful experiment. This chapter begins with some simple definitions of the key measures and metrics concepts, then discusses the criteria for evaluating and selecting measures for an experiment, addresses the process of selection, introduces some of the established sets of metrics, and concludes with how these principles would apply to the example experiment on self-synchronization.

Definitions

Some standard definitions are less than useful. For example, "measurement" is typically defined as "the act of measuring." However, as in other aspects of science, some standard language is necessary. In particular, the terms *attribute*, *measure*, *metric*, and *indicator* are frequently treated as synonymous, when in fact they have different meanings.

Attribute

An attribute is some aspect of an event, situation, person, or object considered important to understanding the subject under study. Examples of interest might include the range of a weapon system, the time required to complete a decision cycle, the number of nodes in a network, or any other factor considered important in the hypotheses and model of an experimentation problem or issue.

Measure

A measure is a standard by which some attribute of interest (extent, dimensions, quantity, etc.) is recorded. For example, weight (an attribute) can be measured in terms of pounds or kilograms; speed (an attribute) can be measured in miles per hour; and time is measured in minutes and seconds.

Measures are the specific form the team expects to use when capturing attributes of interest.

Metric

A metric is the application of a measure to two or more cases or situations. Because experiments are inherently comparative as well as inherently empirical, selection of the metrics is particularly important. These are the ways things will be compared. For example, an experiment about time-critical targeting might include the likelihood of detecting different types of targets, under different conditions, by different types of sensors, and using different fusion tools and techniques. Therefore, one attribute of interest would be the likelihood of detection. The measure would then be the percentage of detections. The metric of interest would be the relative probability of detection across the *syndromes* of target types, detection conditions, sensor arrays, and approaches to fusion. Explaining and understanding these differences in the dependent variable would be the primary focus of the analysis.

Indicators

Measures and metrics apply directly to the attributes of interest. However, direct measurement is not possible in all situations. For example, almost all experts agree that situation awareness is an important element in the quality of military decisionmaking. However, awareness is a cognitive phenomenon that implies not only that some combat support system has access to a set of facts or that they are displayed at a work station, but also that the decisionmakers are aware of those facts. In simple terms, the situation awareness that matters occurs "between the ears." Indicators are indirect measures and metrics. To assess quality of situation awareness, for example, an experimentation team might create a stimulus (insert a new enemy force into a military situation) and look for a behavioral response (discussion of the new threat, planning to counter it, etc.). They might also debrief the key people in a command center to see whether they have perceived the new threat and understand it. The experimenters might want to use an indirect approach and call for a situation briefing to see whether this new factor is included. Regardless of the technique used to generate empirical evidence, that evidence will be indirect and in the form of indicators.

Levels of Measurement

Measurement should always be as precise as is practical. However, understanding the level of precision that can be achieved without distorting what is being observed and measured is important. Four different levels of measurement are possible: nominal, ordinal, interval, and ratio. The level of precision achieved is crucial both for developing an appropriate data analysis plan and also for understanding and interpreting findings.

Nominal measurement means that observations can be assigned to categories, but the categories themselves have no natural order. For example, service training may differ in important ways and may be a factor expected to influence behavior in a command center experiment. However, there is no natural order between Army, Navy, Air Force, and Marine backgrounds. The same is true for gender differences or differences between officers from coalition countries.

Ordinal measurement means that there is a natural order between the categories, but the distances between them have no meaning. Operating environments, for example, might be differentiated in terms of the level of threat and classified as low, medium, and high. The order between these will not change. However, there is no meaningful measure or metric that expresses the size of the difference between these categories. Similarly, the level of expertise typical in a command center might be classified as novice, journeyman, or expert depending on the level of training and experience of its personnel. The rank order is clear, but there is no meaningful way to characterize how much more expert one group is than another.

Interval measurement occurs when the distances between points on a scale are meaningful (can be added and subtracted), but they are anchored arbitrarily (zero has no empirical meaning) and therefore cannot be multiplied. The most common example of an interval measurement scale is the Fahrenheit thermometer. The intervals on this scale are identical and meaningful. Fifty degrees is 10 degrees warmer than 40 degrees, which is precisely the same as the 10-degree difference between 100 degrees and 90 degrees. However, 100 degrees is not twice as hot as 50 degrees. This occurs because zero degrees is not the absence of heat. Similarly, intelligence quotients, which are often used to differentiate between subjects in experiments, are interval scales. Someone with an IQ of 150 is not twice as intelligent as someone with an IQ of 75.

Ratio measurement has both equal level intervals and also a meaningful anchor point (zero is a meaningful value). Numbers of platforms, time required to complete a task, months or years of experience, weapons ranges, and a host of other attributes in the battlespace are legitimate ratio values. As a result, measures and metrics for such attributes can be treated with the most powerful analytic tools available. Whenever possible, therefore, experimentation teams will seek ratio level measures and metrics.

The level of measurement sought and achieved in designing an experiment is important in two significant ways. First, efforts to be overly precise will lead to bad data. If judgements about the quality of military decisions can be rated consistently as successful, marginally successful, and failed, ordinal measurement can be achieved. To assign numeric values that imply interval or ratio measurement to those ordered categories implies information content that does not exist. This will distort any analysis performed on the data and will also undercut the credibility of the research effort. Second, statistical analyses employ tools that assume specific levels of measurement. Applying techniques that make assumptions inconsistent with the information content of the data (for example, ratio techniques to ordinal data) is fraught with peril and very likely to generate misleading results.

Criteria for Measures and Metrics

Selecting specific measures, metrics, and indicators for an experiment requires explicit criteria. While long lists are sometimes offered, selection of the empirical evidence to be collected should always be based on three fundamental criteria: validity, reliability, and credibility. If any of these is compromised, the experiment will not succeed in contributing to the development of knowledge and understanding, and may contribute to unnecessary confusion.

Validity

Simply stated, validity means that the measures, metrics, and indicators employed actually measure what the experimentation team is trying to measure. For example, the likelihood of target detection under specific circumstances can be validly measured by observing the percentage of targets actually detected. Hence, this is a valid measure. On the other hand, many important concepts are much more difficult to measure validly. For example, NATO has been using "normalcy indicators" in Bosnia and Kosovo to recognize when the peace operations have achieved the goal of stabilizing societies and allowing people to go about their business safely. This implies a decision as to what attributes of those societies represent "normalcy" and how empirical evidence (marketplace prices, movement of commerce, attendance at school, etc.) can be collected which reflects a return to normal life. Similarly, the measurement of situation awareness raises serious validity issues since the experimentation team must have a rich and correct understanding of what constitutes high quality situation awareness in order to identify valid ways to measure it. They must develop indicators that reflect what people actually know.

Errors in validity are all too common in DoD experimentation. For example, many efforts have tried to deal with the "timeliness" of the information available by measuring its latency (how old it is before it is available). Age or latency of information is certainly an interesting and potentially important attribute, but it is not timeliness. Timeliness can only be meaningful in terms of some situation or window of opportunity. Age of information is not a valid measure of its timeliness except in the presence of some standard. For example, in a time-critical targeting issue, a standard of reporting information no older than 30 minutes might be seen as important. In that case, latency of information could be converted into the percentage of reports with data of 30 minutes or less and would be a more valid measure in the analysis.

Note also, that more than one measure is often required to achieve validity. If the concept is a complex one, it may have more than one dimension. The example of improved command and control involving both faster and better decisionmaking has already been mentioned. A similar example occurs when flexibility of planning is assessed. A more flexible plan includes more than one way to achieve the military mission, but it also must include the ability to recognize which of these options is available and can be executed successfully. Merely proliferating options is not, by itself, a valid metric for flexibility.

Reliability

Reliability implies that the same value would be reported on an attribute of interest regardless of the observer or the observation method. A metal ruler is more reliable that a rubber one, but not perfectly reliable if major temperature changes can be expected between observations. Reliability is often an issue when the phenomenon under study must be inferred indirectly from indicators or when human perceptions are involved – whether perceptions of subjects, observers, or controllers. Reliability is crucial in science. The design of the observation and data collection systems are largely driven by efforts to ensure reliability.

When possible, direct reliable measures should be selected. However, reliable measures that lack validity are not useful. Modeling and experimenting are commonly criticized for focusing on data that can be easily and reliably measured rather than data that is important – implying that reliability has been chosen over validity. The answer, when reliability problems are likely, lies in the training of observers and collectors and in planning for inter-coder reliability testing. This testing, which needs to occur during training as well as during the conduct of the experiment and related data reduction efforts, is an explicit method for establishing the reliability of the collection and measurement schemes.

The experimentation team also needs to think through the essential elements for reliable measurement. As a simple example, a team that plans to use time-based measures, such as how long after a scenario injection a command center recognizes the event, must be certain to calibrate the clocks and watches being used to record the event and its recognition. Similarly, a team interested in the percentage of situation awareness elements that are reported correctly by members of a watch team must have a simple, reliable standard for which elements of situation awareness need to be covered and how the information presented is to be coded if it is only "partly correct."

Credibility

Beyond the essential issues of validity and reliability, experimentation also requires measures and metrics that are credible to their audiences. *Credibility* means that the measures are believable to those who must understand and act on the results, specifically the research and experimentation community, the decisionmakers who must translate experiment results into policies, programs, and plans of action, as well as the military subject matter experts and "operators" who must learn and act on the knowledge generated. In the social science literature, credibility with expert audiences is termed "face validity." Novel, subtle, or esoteric measures must be developed and presented in ways that are transparent to all these audiences. Similarly, careless labeling of measures and metrics that expose them to surface misunderstandings or criticisms can lose credibility.

The systems and communications communities' use of the term *situation awareness* provides a good example of measurement that lacks credibility. In many cases, they have chosen to use that term to refer to the quality of the information present in displays and data files. Hence, good situation awareness meant that all the entities of interest were present in the information system, available for presentation, and could be displayed in ways that distinguished them from one another (armor would be distinguished from supply convoys, fast movers from other types of aircraft, warships from commercial vessels, etc.). However, the research community, which understands situation awareness to be what people know (not what is available to them from machines), did not find this approach to measuring situation awareness credible. Similarly, many military personnel, who understand situation awareness to extend beyond the "who is where" picture to include obvious military developments in the future (the turning of a flank, an imminent breakthrough, an urgent need for water, etc.) also found this approach lacking.

Need for All Three Criteria

Transformational experimentation teams need to pay attention to all three criteria. Lack of validity means that the experiment cannot yield meaningful results. Lack of reliability means that the data cannot be trusted, so the results should not be believed. Lack of credibility means that the results will not be believed. Hence, selecting measures and metrics is a process where the highest possible standards must be used.

Process of Measure and Metric Selection

While every experiment will present different challenges and opportunities and every team of experimenters will need to exercise both creativity and judgement, there are some processes that have proven useful in the past. These processes should be a starting point for selecting measures and metrics.

Anchoring in the Initial Model

The experimentation team will want to anchor its efforts in the initial model, which was developed as a result of their studies of previous research and their efforts to build meaningful sets of propositions and hypotheses. In many cases, the same variables represented in that model will have been present in prior research and experimentation. Hence, the measures and metrics employed in prior efforts can be considered as candidates. Note that prior work may contains both good and bad precedents. While the process of accumulating knowledge will benefit if the same or similar measures can be employed, precedents should not be employed at the expense of validity, reliability, or credibility. If the measurement approach in prior work appears flawed, then the team should take that as an important lesson learned, not an example to be followed.

The initial model and its first executable form are also simple sources for the list of concepts that need measuring. It should include definitions, though they may be too abstract to employ without further work to make them operationally meaningful. This will sometimes be the first time that measures are translated into specific metrics or that the need for more than one metric in order to capture the full concept under analysis is recognized.

Dependent Variables First

Since the dependent variables are the objective functions for the experiment and its analysis, specifying their definitions, measures, and metrics is the first task. Note that this discussion presumes that more than one dependent variable will be relevant in almost all transformational experimentation. This premise is based on three assumptions. First, most important concepts underlying dependent variables are multidimensional. The classic "better command and control" composed of more correct decisions made more quickly is an excellent example. Second, layered systems of dependent variables are often valuable aids to understanding and analysis. A classic example is the MORS approach of layers of measures of performance (MOP) for systems (human and machine) supporting layers of measures of C2 effectiveness (MOCE), supporting layers of force effectiveness (MOFE), which support layers of policy effectiveness (MOPE). Third, most dependent variables should be collected across at least three echelons of command for diagnostic purposes. Hence, an analysis intended to test propositions at the joint task force level should at least be informed by data at the component and CINC levels of command. For example, an effort to measure "clear and consistent command intent" in joint task force performance needs to look up and down at least one echelon and examine communications and collaboration across levels in order to gauge clarity and consistency.

The definitions of each variable of interest need to be reviewed carefully. If the concept is simple, it may have a single, direct measure. For example, decision cycle time can be measured validly, reliably, and credibly by a team that is properly trained and has access to reliable, calibrated clocks and the relevant command center activities. Similarly, the number of people participating in a collaboration session can be recorded directly, provided that the term participation is clearly defined, perhaps as workstations linked to the session.

In many cases, however, the dependent variable will be multidimensional. No single attribute will validly cover the entire concept. For example, future command and control systems will need to be adaptable. However, that adaptability may involve changes in structure, participation, or work processes. Hence, an experimentation team interested in that phenomenon would need a set of measures, not just a single one.

The purposes of specifying the entire measurement system for the dependent variable(s) of interest before trying to complete the entire set are to ensure (a) that the full set is specified when the independent and intervening variables' measures are chosen and (b) the dependent variables are fully independent of them. If the dependent variables of interest are somehow defined or measured in ways that cause them to overlap with the independent or intervening variables, the experiment will be confounded and its results will be confusing at best, and meaningless at worst.

As each measure and metric is considered, the experimentation team needs to review the simple mantra of "validity, reliability, and credibility." The question on validity is whether the measure or set of measures selected really represents the concept, the whole concept, and nothing but the concept under study. The question on reliability is whether the same events, situations, attributes, or behaviors will always be recorded and scored the same way, regardless of when, where, or by whom (or by which machine) the data are captured. The issue on credibility is whether the measure will be accepted by, or can be explained clearly to, the three key audiences: the research and experimentation community, the decisonmaking community, and the operational community.

Dependent and Intervening Variables

Once the proper set of dependent variables is articulated and any requisite changes made to the hypotheses or propositions under study, the remaining variables should be subjected to the same process, with one exception. Beyond validity, reliability, and credibility, the other variables need to be examined for independence, both from one another and from the set of dependent variables already chosen. Where independence is in question, the data analysis plan will need to include empirical tests of the strength of association between the variables of interest. Moreover, provision should be made for analytic techniques that can provide statistical processes that can compensate if independence cannot be achieved.

Feasibility Testing: Data Analysis and Data Collection Planning

As the full set of variables is identified and measures, metrics, and indicators are selected, they need to be organized into a system that will inform the data analysis and data collection plans. This process raises a number of important practical considerations, including:

- Whether the measures and metrics will yield data sets ready for analysis on all the issues under study;

- Whether the experimentation team has access to all the data and information necessary to support the analyses;

- Whether the data and information needed can be captured cost effectively;

- Whether adequate numbers of collectors, recorders (human and machine), and controllers are available;

- Whether the schedule and resources for training, collection, data reduction, inter-coder reliability testing, and archiving are adequate.

In essence, this practical review enables the team to complete the data analysis and data collection plans while also forcing the experimenters to think through their resource requirements.

Established Measures and Metric Systems

While each experiment is different and each experimentation team will need to be both creative and thoughtful about the specific measures and metrics they choose to employ, there are some established frameworks that may be useful, particularly when command and control issues are central to the research effort. Both the MORS categories of measures and the NATO *Code of Best Practice for C2 Assessment* have been mentioned earlier and can be used to understand the classic approaches. However, those classic sources can be brought up to date and better focused by looking at some of the more recent applications and approaches. Those are briefly discussed below, including an assessment of their strengths and weaknesses, as well as references to where more information can be located.

Network Centric Warfare Value Chain

The elements of one established system, the Network Centric Warfare value chain, are illustrated in Figure 2-1.[1] This approach employs several layered concepts:

- The beginning point is the quality of the information and knowledge available within the command and control system.

- Information quality follows the metrics developed more than 20 years ago in the Headquarters Effectiveness Assessment Tool (HEAT) to track the completeness, correctness, currency, consistency, and precision of the data items and information statements available.

- Knowledge quality here refers to the prior knowledge embedded in the command and control system such as templates for adversary forces, assumptions about entities (ranges, weapons, etc.), and doctrinal assumptions used to infer future adversary actions (intentions).

- Awareness refers to information and knowledge as they are known by the individuals using the command and control system. Awareness is always in the cognitive domain and must be measured using indicators such as survey instruments and debriefings, or inferred from behavior.

Taken together, information, knowledge, and individual awareness constitute the *richness* of the content available in the command and control system. *Reach*, on the other hand, depends on the ability to share information, knowledge, and awareness.

- Shared information and knowledge can be measured in almost exactly the same way as individual information and knowledge (completeness, correctness, currency, consistency, and precision). However, new dimensions must be considered: what fractions of the relevant command and control system users have access, what delays may occur in that access, how well the total system is informed (what is known to the members), and how well the typical (average or median) user is informed.

- Similarly, shared awareness must be understood in terms of these four new dimensions, but the indicators will focus on what individuals perceive, not what is available to them from their systems.

- Shared understanding, which builds in the information, knowledge, and awareness to define relevant cause and effect relationships as well as temporal dynamics and puts them into an operational context that defines the threats and opportunities relevant to each actor and their opportunities to influence the military situation, is also an important element of reach.

The command and control processes supported by reach and richness form a hierarchical ladder that moves from decisionmaking in the military context through synchronization and mission or task effectiveness to the overarching level of policy effectiveness.

• Decisionmaking effectiveness has two
  fundamental components: quality of the
  decision process and quality of the decision.

  - Quality of the decision process can be
    measured in several ways. These include
    issues such as the number and variety of
    participants, the variety of alternatives
    considered, and the explicitness of the
    criteria applied.

  - Quality of decision measures often
    includes the speed with which the decision
    is made, but should also include some way
    of assessing the decision itself – fast
    decisionmaking should not be confused with
    good decisionmaking. The quality of military
    decisions is only known in the real world
    after the fact. In experiments, it is common
    to use panels of subject matter experts to
    judge decision quality, both before and after
    the fact. The key here is to ensure
    objectivity – bias due to interpersonal
    relationships, service doctrine, or other
    factors should be screened out whenever
    possible. Blind judging can be helpful.

- Synchronization is a factor that has long been appreciated in judging command and control performance, but is only now coming to be understood well enough to measure in a reliable and valid way. Synchronization refers to "purposeful arrangement in time and space."[2] The fundamental scale that has emerged is the percentage of the elements or assets of a force that are (a) conflicted (interfering with one another or limiting one another's actions), (b) deconflicted, or (c) synergistic (multiplying the effects of one another).

- Measures of mission or task effectiveness, which include classic force effectiveness measures (casualty ratios, territorial control, etc.) when classic force or attrition missions are assigned, form a still higher or more comprehensive layer of measures. When strategy-to-task structures are used, they provide the framework for this class of measure.

- Policy Effectiveness forms the topmost layer in this framework. As mission complexity has grown and purely military activities have become subordinate to political, humanitarian, counter-drug, counter-terrorism, counter-insurgency, and peace operations; the need to assess overall success (rather than military success) has become increasingly important.

The Network Centric Warfare value chain provides a rich source for thinking through the set of metrics relevant to a particular experiment. However, it is only one such source. Most data collection and data analysis plans should consider more than one approach and ultimately select a set of measures and metrics that make unique sense for their problem or hypotheses.

Effects-Oriented Measures and Metrics

An Australian team (Seymour et. al.)[3] has recently introduced an alternative hierarchical arrangement of measures (Figure 7-1) predicated on the assumption that effects-based operations (EBO) is the concept that best underlies future military operations. This approach asserts that there are five crucial layers:

- Data Superiority (data collected);

- Information Superiority (information quality);

- Knowledge Superiority (situation awareness);

- Decision Superiority (decision quality); and

- Effects Superiority (achieving intent).

Unfortunately, this approach introduces some language that is inconsistent with the NCW usage in the United States and mixes ideas from the NCW work with that of Professor Endsley (2000), but it is reported intelligently and provides comparative results as the basis for suggesting a new approach.

Figure 7-1. Hierarchy of Outcomes

Headquarters Effectiveness Assessment Tool (HEAT)

The longest surviving approach to measurement of command and control, HEAT, originated 20 years ago and has been applied to real warfighting cases, exercises, and experiments, and still underlies work at U.S. Joint Forces Command and in the *NATO Code of Best practice for C2 Assessments*.[4] HEAT organizes the command and control process into several elements and posits a variety of indicators for each element. The elements considered include:

- Monitoring the battlespace – facts known to the information system, scored for completeness, correctness, currency, consistency, and precision;

- Understanding the battlespace – perceptions and understandings of the battlespace, scored for completeness, correctness, time horizon, and consistency;

- Alternatives considered – scored for variety and number of perspectives;

- Predictions made – scored for variety and number, completeness of alternative futures considered;

- Decisions made – not scored, recorded for later comparison with outcomes for mission accomplishment;

- Directives generated – scored for clarity and consistency with decisions made;

- Reports issued – scored for correctness and consistency; and

- Queries for information – scored for response rate, response time, and correctness of response.

All HEAT categories are also supported by speed metrics designed to learn how long the command and control process steps have taken. More recently (in the past 2 years) they have also been supported by measures focused on the degree and quality of collaboration in the command and control processes.

Because it has been widely applied, HEAT has also demonstrated a couple of principles that all experimentation teams should bear in mind. First,

HEAT experience underscores the importance of collecting data at echelons above and below those under detailed study. For example, learning whether directives or reports were clear can only be done by comparing what the authors meant to convey with what the recipients understood. Second, HEAT applications have made it clear that data on automated command and control processes can be taken automatically, but that human-centric command and control processes can only be captured properly by teams of well-trained human observers. In addition, HEAT experience has made it clear that the perceptions of observers, controllers, participants, and support personnel will differ (often widely) and may differ from the empirical evidence. Hence, rich data analysis and data collection plans that include all these perspectives are essential.

Example Application: Self-Synchronization Experiment

The discovery experiment in self-synchronization introduced in the last chapter makes an excellent practical example for developing measures, metrics, and indicators. The first task is to make a list of the variables of interest, which are really the attributes for which measurement is needed. As Figure 6-1 shows, there were 12 attributes identified in the initial descriptive model:

- Effective self-synchronization (the dependent variable of interest);

- High quality shared situation awareness (intervening variable);

- Congruent command intent (intervening variable);

- Trust (intervening variable);

- Common perceptual filters (intervening variable);

- High quality situation awareness (intervening variable);

- Collaborative command and control processes (intervening variable);

- Competence (intervening variable);

- Empowering leadership (intervening variable);

- High quality information (independent variable);

- Information availability (independent variable); and

- Shared knowledge and experience (independent variable).

All of these variables will need to be understood at the measure and metric level, whether they are to be manipulated or controlled in the experiment. Even factors that will be controlled in the experiment design will need scales and values so the experimenters know that these variables have achieved and maintained those values, and so that later experiments (where they may be manipulated) can be informed properly by these results.

Dependent Variable:
Effective Self-Synchronization

Identification of measures and metrics should always begin with the dependent variable, both to ensure that the other variables are defined in ways that are not confounded with the dependent, and also to ensure that the focus of the experiment has been properly captured. The project team found that little experimentation had been done on this topic and most of the work on defining the term remained immature. Hence, the experimentation team focused its first efforts at clear, precise definition. The term has at least three elements: "effective," "synchronization," and "self."

Work began with the concept of synchronization. This has been defined as "purposeful arrangement in and across time and space."[5] While helpful, this definition is not operational. It does not tell a research team what to look for in order to determine whether one case is at all "more synchronized" than another.

The most fundamental dimension underlying the concept emerges from conflicted situations (units and activities that interfere with one another, down to and including fratricide) through de-conflicted situations (boundaries, schedules, and other control measures are used to prevent interference, but units and activities therefore function independently and also constrain one another) to synergistic situations where activities and units interact to generate effects or mission accomplishments greater than the linear sum of their parts. This approach has the advantage of including the concept of *effective* within the meaning of synchronization. Moreover, the experimentation team stressed that synergistic activities and units are supporting one another, not just working within the same space and time period. Adopting this approach, the experimentation team selected two fundamental measures for "effective synchronization:"

- For a given period of time, the percentage of activities (missions or tasks) that are conflicted, de-conflicted, and synergistic; and

- For a given period of time, the percentage of units whose actions are conflicted, de-conflicted, and synergistic.

These two measures cross-check one another. They also recognize that synchronization occurs over time and must be integrated over time to be meaningful. They will require the ability to identify tasks (as in the concept of strategy to task, but including non-military tasks such as informational, political, economic, and social activities that are significant in accomplishing the mission) as well as a consistent definition of *unit* that applies to the forces and other organizations involved. The basic mathematical formulation of these two metrics is shown below.[6]

$$S = \frac{\sum_{\iota = 1}^{n-1} V_\iota}{C^n_2}$$

where,

S = degree of synchronization $[-1 \leq S \leq +1]$
C^n_2 = combination of n things taken 2 at a time
V_ι = 1 if the ith pair is in a state of synergy
    0 if the ith pair is in a state of neutrality
    -1 if the ith pair is in a state of interference
n = case number

Knowing what synchronization means helps to define *self*-synchronization because it is an essential element of the concept, a necessary yet insufficient condition. Clearly, synchronization can be achieved by centralized control. For example, U.S. Air Force Air Tasking Orders (ATO) synchronize a variety of different types of aircraft engaged in a variety of missions and tasks by providing a centralized mechanism that blends the efforts of all the forces. These "order" types of mechanisms, as well as directives that focus on specific military objectives under integrated schedules, discourage many kinds of initiative.[7] Classic self-synchronization occurs when leaders and commanders throughout the battlespace are able to generate synergy based on their shared (a) training and experience, (b) understanding of the commander's intent, and (c) awareness and understanding of the situation.

For example, during the Civil War and the Napoleonic Wars, commanders often followed the rule that their forces should "march to the sound of the guns," largely because they seldom had good intelligence on where the enemy force was located or even where the other friendly forces were at a given point in time. Hence, this rule of thumb made it possible for forces to concentrate in the presence of an enemy without first establishing communications or developing a plan to integrate their actions.

The experimentation team in this case decided that self-synchronization would be recognized when the commander's mission type orders and the forces involved could be scored as synergistic in terms of units and activities. Hence, the experimenters incurred an obligation to be able to capture all directives (from written plans through verbal commands and consultations between commanders) in their data collection plan, and also to create the capability to distinguish mission type orders from others. Therefore, part of the effort to make self-synchronization operational will need to include developing, testing, and revising coding rules that can identify mission type orders and count the missions and tasks assigned, as well as the units assigned to them.

Independent Variables

The working model of the problem (Figure 6-1) identified only three true independent variables (factors expected to impact the dependent variable, but not driven by other factors in the model): information quality, information availability, and shared knowledge and experience. The first two of them, however, were seen as interacting with one another and being mutually reinforcing. That is, the quality of the available information was expected to be higher if that information could be made available widely, and the breadth of availability was seen as increasing the quality of the information as the participants shared and discussed it. These three factors were seen as so important to effective self-synchronization that they would need to be assured by the experiment design in order to activate the processes that the experiment would focus on, namely the interactions between the participants.

High quality information is well-defined in the HEAT tradition. High quality information is drawn from the monitoring function, which is located in the information domain and consists of facts and basic inferences about what *is* and what *is becoming*, rather than the richer inferences needed to convert those sets of facts into situation awareness and understandings. This perspective was seen as appropriate to the problem under analysis since the initial model distinguishes between the quality of information and the quality of situation awareness. The key measures suggested in this part of the HEAT model are:

- Completeness – information is available about all the entities and situations of interest to the decisionmakers (metrics focus on percentage complete);

- Correctness – there is no false information and the uncertainty surrounding that information is explicitly known (metrics focus on percentage correct);

- Currency – the information has no time lag and the time lags that do exist are known (metrics focus on latency of information items and percentage within command standards established for types of information);

- Consistency – there is no difference between the information sets known to different parts of the information system (metrics focus on percentage of items consistent); and

- Precision – whether the information item has adequate precision for some specific application (metrics focus on percentage of items within the command standard such as targeting quality versus adversary posture in the battlespace).

Each of these groups of measures already has detailed working definitions in the HEAT system. Moreover, training materials exist from prior applications. However, every experiment has unique needs and features, so even these "tried and true" sets of measures were scrubbed in detail to ensure their relevance and focus. For example, establishing the command standards for latency on information of different types requires assessment. Prior applications had established acceptable time-critical targeting latency at 60 minutes based on the time required to process the information, assign assets, and strike the target. However, only a fraction of the relevant targets were being struck successfully with this standard, so the subject matter experts working with the experimentation team recommended this threshold be reduced to 30 minutes.

Because high quality information was seen as a necessary yet insufficient condition for effective self-synchronization, the experimentation team decided that its values should be directly controlled in the experiment. They did not, however, want to lose the very real features of uncertainty and a lack of precision as factors that the subjects should consider. Hence, they instructed those developing the experimentation environments (supporting scenario information – see the next chapter) that completeness should be at 80 percent, correctness at 90 percent, currency within command standards at 80 percent, consistency at 100 percent for what was available (no differences in the underlying data sets) for U.S. forces and at 80 percent for coalition forces, while precision would reflect the capabilities of the reporting sensors. This last assumption reflected concerns that the participants would have prior knowledge of the reliability and capabilities of the sensor suites in use. Therefore, using artificial values for precision would lead to confusion and might reduce the credibility of the experiment in the eyes of some subjects.

Because information quality would vary across time within the boundaries established by the experimenters, it also had to be recorded so it could be included in the data analysis plan and its hypothesized impact on other factors assessed statistically. In this case, this meant monitoring the databases and injections into them and taking measures of central tendency (means, since the metrics adopted are ratio measures) and dispersion (standard deviations). Ideally, these would be tracked continuously, minute by minute. However, given the indirect impact of the quality of information, the decision was made to record data hourly throughout the experiment.

Information availability, also seen as a necessary yet insufficient condition for effective self-synchronization, was another factor that the experimentation team wanted to control, but not at perfect levels. The measure that matters is workstation access, meaning who can interact with which parts of the database at any given time and collaborate with others about the available information. Connectivity was established for this experiment at 95 percent, with randomly assigned breaks ranging from 1 minute to 40 minutes across linkages. Participants were to be given the capability to check on outages and ground truth about their existence and correct them to within plus or minus 30 percent of their length, but only if they inquired.

The experimentation team also noted that information availability was a potentially crucial factor that they were deliberately controlling in this experiment, but which was worthy of further research. Hence, they noted that it should be explored further, both in their own sensitivity analyses after the experiment and in later experimentation on similar issues.

As noted earlier, *shared knowledge and experience* was the final truly independent variable seen as a fundamentally necessary yet insufficient condition for self-synchronization. This is a very difficult factor to control, but it is also seen as a powerful determinant of other factors in the model, such as creating common perceptual filters, perceptions of competence, and willingness of leaders to empower subordinate commanders.

The first inclination of the experimentation team was to look for existing military organizations in order to ensure that their teams of subjects had a high level of shared knowledge and experience. However, they soon recognized that (a) such teams would be difficult to obtain as subjects, (b) existing military teams are impacted by rotation and may or may not have rich shared knowledge and experience, and (c) the settings and military missions for this experiment may reduce the relevance of the shared knowledge and experience of existing teams.

The second approach considered was informed by one of the social scientists on the experimentation team. She pointed out that small groups create shared knowledge and experience as they work on problems and that this process generates a set of artifacts that capture their efforts. This set of artifacts includes specialized language, heuristic approaches to the problem that increase team productivity, knowledge of one another's expertise and perspectives, as well as roles within the team. Taking this perspective, the experimenters decided that they would seek to create the shared knowledge and experience within their teams of subjects during training. *This solution to the problem illustrates the value of having a multidisciplinary team.* While they still felt a strong need to have military professionals as subjects, they felt they could, by having the groups work a series of problems together during the training phase of the experiment, create a meaningful level of relevant shared knowledge and experience. This decision obviously implied a link to subject training, demanding that subject teams be created as early as possible and training would need to ensure a number and variety of relevant problems where those teams would work together. *The training impact of this decision* about *controlling shared knowledge and experience is an excellent example of the close linkage between the elements of an experimentation plan.*

However, deciding on an approach to establishing shared knowledge and experience within the teams of subjects is not the same as creating the appropriate measures and metrics. Regardless of how well the training creates opportunities for creating these factors, the subject teams are likely to vary in shared knowledge and experience. Moreover, these may change during the experiment as the subjects gain more experience working together. Hence, good definitions and measures will be needed.

The team noted that knowledge and experience are partly determined before the teams come together for the experiment. Hence, data will be needed about the individual's background and training. Fortunately, they had access to a questionnaire developed by the Information Superiority Working Group for an experiment conducted at U.S. JFCOM in 2001.[8] This instrument includes the length of professional military experience, Service, branch, military, and civilian educational background, computer literacy, assignments, command experience, command center experience, combat experience, and other factors that might impact performance. However, the new thinking implied by the self-synchronization experiment is focused on how these background factors can be compared to identify teams with more or less shared knowledge and experience. In this case, the team decided the questionnaire was adequate for data collection, but noted that the data analysis plan would need to use some clustering techniques to measure closeness of prior education, training, and experience. Multidimensional scaling was the recommended approach, though the number of teams and individuals involved was also recognized as a under-developed factor in the analysis plan that might lead to different choices later in the process.

Another other key issue remained – how to measure shared knowledge and experience at the end of training and during the experiment itself. The decision was made to rely on two cross-checking techniques: self-reporting and behavioral observation. These two very different techniques were chosen because this is a difficult measurement problem and because neither technique can be assumed to be fully valid or reliable by itself.

The self-reporting instrument focused on each team member's perceptions of what they have in common with others on the team as well as relevant differences from them. It also asked about how close the individual's perceptions of the experiment's situations and approaches to military problems are to those of other members of the team. This latter section of the questionnaire was designed to reflect changes in shared knowledge and experience as the group worked together through training problems and experiment trials. Provision was also made in the schedule of the experiment for follow-up interviews with individual members of the subject teams to clarify their answers where necessary.

Behavioral observation was planned around the groups' creating artifacts such as specialized language, heuristic approaches to problem solving, common ground among team members, etc. This entailed training the observers in recognizing the emergence, use, and growth of those artifacts that indicated increasing shared knowledge and experience, as well as those behaviors (challenges, miscommunication, etc.) indicating a lack of shared knowledge and experience. This required another adjustment to the training schedule and an instrument on which to record relevant behaviors.

Intervening Variables

The eight other variables being explicitly considered are intervening variables believed to impact the dependent variable, but also influenced by one of more other factors in the conceptual model.

Common Perceptual Filters are a product of shared knowledge and experience. Hence, the decision was made to handle them as part of the questionnaire on that topic. The specific technique selected was to offer key terms and images from each of the operational vignettes used to drive the experiment and have the subjects provide their interpretations of what each means and the relative importance of each term or object in the situation. Responses were scored on commonality, not on correctness.

Competence, in the context of this experiment, is really perception of competence. The assumption is that superior commanders will be reluctant to empower junior commanders with mission type orders and responsibility for self-synchronized actions unless they perceive those junior commanders as competent. Hence, this issue will need to be addressed with a survey instrument. Again, the decision was made to include issues of the competence of other actors on the same questionnaire used to assess shared knowledge and experience and common perceptual filters.

Trust is also a perceptual issue and was also added to the questionnaire. Trust, however, is often situational. Hence, several questions were needed to establish levels of trust on different topics such as (a) willingness and ability to provide complete and correct information, (b) capability to develop an independent plan of action, (c) willingness to ask for assistance when needed, and (d) willingness to seize the initiative when appropriate.

Empowering Leadership is difficult to control as it results not only from the perceptions that commanders have of their subordinates, but also personal leadership style. As a consequence, the decision was made to capture this factor through behavioral observation. A rich literature exists on leadership and it was researched to find both operational definitions of empowering leadership and also indicators of that behavior. The key definition focuses on the distinction between consultative and directive approaches. The key indicators focus on the extent to which the leader seeks prior knowledge about and explicit control over decisions that are fully within the responsibility of the subordinate, and the extent to which collaboration and problem solving between subordinate commanders is encouraged and accepted. This subject also needed to be included in the training plan for the experiment.

Collaborative Command and Control Processes were available to the subjects throughout the experiment, except when their connectivity was interrupted (see the discussion of information availability), which was recorded for analysis. Hence, the major difference is how much collaboration each team used. This can be measured directly by instrumenting and recording the collaboration tool.

High Quality Situation Awareness is a difficult concept in the abstract. Fortunately, an operational approach to this issue was developed in the DARPA Command Post of the Future Program, vetted by the Information Superiority Working Group, and applied again within the JFCOM series of Limited Objective Experiments. This approach recognizes that awareness is what people know. It decomposes the knowledge needed to understand a military problem into factors:

- Capability and intentions of own, adversary, and uncommitted forces;

- Missions assigned to those forces as well as constraints on them;

- Knowledge of the environment (physical, weather, political, economic, social, and other relevant factors such as International Organizations, NGOs, etc);

- Time and space relationships;

- Uncertainties about the data and information available; and

- Threats and Opportunities for all the actors involved.

In the approach adopted, each of these factors is *pre-solved* into an ideal solution by subject matter experts. The subjects complete a questionnaire about their perceptions of the situation during selected breaks in the experiments. These answers are then compared with the "school solution" generated earlier. Scores are reported as a percentage of the correct solution, with counts made of both erroneous perceptions and correct relevant perceptions not in the school solution.

High Quality Shared Situational Awareness can be inferred by comparing the situation awareness questionnaires from the subjects assigned to the same team. Shared items are those that are correct across members of the team. Different scores can be expected across different pairs so that scoring should be available in case one member of a team turns out to have a very different awareness from the larger team. Incorrect shared perceptions should also be scored separately as they are likely to influence the overall performance of the team.

Congruent Command Intent, the last intervening variable, can be scored by comparison of the statements of intent, plans, directives, and orders given at different echelons and across different units or functions. The standard for comparison is the senior commander. However, pair-wise comparison is the driving metric. In a self-synchronized world, the lower level commanders may well be making decisions that are consistent with one another, but are not identical to the original command intent generated at senior levels when different information was available.

Conclusion

The length and complexity of this example illustrates the difficulty and importance of serious, upfront work on measures and metrics. Experiments that fail to invest in these crucial topics are very likely to fall far short of their goals and purposes. Clarity of definition; validity, reliability, and credibility of measures and metrics; preparation and planning for data collection and analysis; and training for subjects, observers, and others supporting the experiment are all heavily impacted by the quality of thinking in this crucial arena.

---

[1]Alberts, David S., John J. Gartska, Richard E. Hayes, and David A. Signori. *Understanding Information Age Warfare*. Washington, DC: CCRP. 2001. p76.

[2]*Understanding Information Age Warfare*. p206.

[3]Seymour, Robert, Yi Yue, Anne-Marie Grisogono, and Michael Bonner. "Example of Use of a 'Knowledge Superiority' Based Framework for C4ISR Metrics." Land Operations Division Defence Science and Technology Organisation. 2002.

[4]*Headquarters Effectiveness Assessment Tool "HEAT" User's Manual*. McLean, VA: Defense Systems, Inc. 1984.

[5]*Understanding Information Age Warfare*. p206. Note this has been adapted by the ISWG to emphasize "across."

[6]*Understanding Information Age Warfare*. p231.

[7]Alberts, David S. and Richard E. Hayes. *Command Arrangements for Peace Operations*. Washington, DC: NDU Press. 1995.

[8]See Appendix D.

CHAPTER 8

Scenarios

What is a Scenario?

The NATO *Code of Best Practice for C2 Assessment* (Revised Edition, 2002) defines the term *scenario* as "a description of the area, the environment, means, objectives, and events related to a conflict or a crisis during a specific timeframe suited for satisfactory study objectives and problem analysis directives." That volume also discusses the topic in considerable detail and is recommended as a source for those who are new to dealing with the subject. However, its focus is both broader (all types of analysis) and narrower (primarily command and control, though much of its guidance can be applied to a range of military analyses) than the focus here on transformational experimentation.

The same source goes on to argue that scenarios consist of four primary elements – "a context (e.g., characterization of a geopolitical situation), the participants (e.g., intentions, capabilities, of blue, red, and others), the environment (e.g., natural – weather and manmade – mines), and the evolution of events in time." It also notes that "the purpose of scenarios is to ensure that the analysis is informed by the appropriate range of opportunities to observe the relevant variables and their interrelationships." This drives home the point that scenarios are tools, not ends in themselves. As such they need to be crafted, selected, or adapted to ensure that they support the goals of the experiment.

Scenarios in Transformation Experimentation

Scenarios provide the substantive focus and boundaries for experimentation. This makes them a crucial element in planning for success. Herein also reside the core dangers for scenarios in experimentation. On the one hand, if they are overly specific, the experiment may not examine all the important propositions or generate data on all the relevant factors and relationships. On the other hand, if they are too general, the experiment may fail to generate adequate data and information to support genuine analysis and learning.

No Single Scenario

Note that the term *scenarios* is always used here in the plural. This reflects a fundamental fact: *no single scenario is likely to be sufficient to support a meaningful experiment*. The use of a single scenario, even one that has been carefully crafted to focus on the key issues in an experiment, invites suboptimization and narrows the range of applicability for the findings. Academic research, which is intended to develop knowledge over long time periods and therefore focuses primarily on incremental additions to knowledge, can afford this luxury. However, transformational military experimentation cannot. Reliance on a single scenario means that the resulting knowledge and models of what has been observed will be optimized for that scenario at the expense of the range of other situations and missions where the military will be employed. During the Cold War, when the U.S. was primarily focused on the Soviet and Warsaw Pact threats and had decades to study their orders of battle, training, doctrine, and materiel, single scenario experiments and analyses made some sense. However, their limits became obvious when American forces had to contend with very different threats and missions in Vietnam. Weapons systems, force structure, doctrine, training, and other items that had been optimized for heavy force-on-force combat in Europe and Korea were less than ideal and had to be altered in fundamental ways.

Defining the Scenario Space

The range of threats and missions relevant to transformational experimentation today are displayed in Figure 8-1, Scenario Threat Space.[1] The vertical axis identifies the sources of threats facing the U.S., from classic nation states with military organizations down through non-state actors (e.g., Palestinians) through organizations (e.g., terrorists, drug cartels, illegal corporate actors) to loosely linked groups (e.g., anti-globalization demonstrators, ethnic groups in turmoil) to threats that arise from natural phenomenon (e.g., AIDS, hurricanes, earthquakes).

Scenario Type

- US-led Military Warfare (Type 1)
- Mostly Coalition, Heavily Restricted Rules of Engagement (ROE) (Type 2)
- Coalition/Interagency Support to Civilian Operations (Type 3)
- Homeland/Border Security (Type 3A)

Conflict ◄─── Mechanism of Engagement ───► Cooperation

	Use of Military Force (Threat or use of US and coalition military force to defend national interests)	Policing / Monitoring (Use of US military to support peacekeeping and complex contingency operations to ensure a secure environment)	Supporting Civilian Missions (Collaboration of US military with civilian entities to further US national interests)
Nation States · Countries · Alliances · Ad hoc coalitions	• Desert Shield/Desert Storm (Iraq) • Uphold Democracy (Haiti)	• UNMIH (Haiti) • Joint Endeavor (Bosnia) • INTERFET (East Timor)	• MIA Recovery Operations
Sub-National Actors · Ethnic groups · Guerrilla groups · Refugees	• Allied Force (Kosovo) • Guardian Retrieval (DRC NEO) • Silver Anvil (Sierra Leone NEO)	• Restore Hope (Somalia) • Joint Guardian (Kosovo) • Essential Harvest (Macedonia)	• Support Hope (Rwanda) • Shining Hope (Kosovo) • Provide Comfort (Kurds)
Organizations · Transnational criminal organizations · Terrorist groups · International business	• Laser Strike (Andean Drug War) • Enduring Freedom (Bin Laden)	• Caribbean Drug Interdiction • Athens Olympic Games security • Internet use to counter terrorist groups	• Noble Eagle (homeland security) • Homeland BW/CW anti-terrorist consequence management
Individuals/Networks · Globalization protestors · Currency speculators · Computer hackers · Migrants	• Maritime interception of new influx of Cuban or Haitian migrants • Special operations to capture terrorist or neutralize a small cell	• Garden Plot (Los Angeles riots) • Capture of CIA Assassin (Kansi) • Globalization protests (WTO, G-8, IMF, etc.)	
Systemic Challenges · Infectious diseases · Natural disasters · Global warming		• Quarantine to control domestic outbreak of Ebola virus	• Fuerte Apoyo (Hurricane Mitch) • Avid Response (Turkey Earthquake) • Forest fire containment (Mexico/Central America)

Figure 8-1. Scenario Threat Space

The horizontal axis defines the types of control mechanisms the U.S., and particularly the U.S. military, may have to employ to be effective against these very different threats. Military operations are clearly relevant to fighting nation states, but decline in relevance as the threat shifts to sources that do not have organized military forces. In current terms, defeating Taliban and organized formations of al-Qaeda forces was a relatively straightforward military task, but those operations have ushered in a much more difficult, and potentially much longer and more complex, set of operations. Other missions today place the military in roles where their primary functions are monitoring and providing policing services. Many peace operations, some interventions, and humanitarian assistance missions outside U.S. borders often require this orientation, at least during their initial phases. Finally, and perhaps most important, many missions today require major efforts in cooperation, not only with nation states (allies, host governments, etc.), but also with international organizations, private volunteer organizations, general populations, and even media organizations.

While some individuals in the military (both U.S. and foreign) would prefer a simpler world in which the only task of the armed forces is to "fight and win the nation's wars," this yearning for a "golden age" is illusory. Even at the height of the Cold War, the first mission of the U.S. Armed Forces was to *deter* major conflicts. Today that tradition continues, but has been expanded into "shaping" the operating environment in ways that seek to prevent or limit overt conflicts and minimize the risks to U.S. lives (including military lives) and property.

As the understanding of effects-based operations grows and as it is incorporated into military planning and operations, the capability of military organizations to employ effective communications and persuasion to shape the environment and gain cooperation will come into sharper focus. Examination of recent history certainly supports the idea that U.S. forces must be able to carry out a wide range of missions and employ a variety of means in order to be effective.

The matrix of threats and control mechanisms makes is appear that the variety of threat sources and ways of carrying out military missions can be segregated neatly. However, the reality is that they have become inextricably mixed and connected. The U.S. Marine Corps concept of a "three block war" in which they expect to be engaged in combat operations in one part of a city, enforcing curfews and disarming the population close by, while providing humanitarian assistance in a third area of the same metropolitan area is a graphic portrayal of this reality. The luxury of having specialized equipment and different forces for each type of mission will only occur in sterile position papers. Realistic thinking about the elements of mission capability packages and DOTMLPF initiatives will have to face this complex reality. Hence, transformational experiments must not be based on a single scenario that only encourages us to put our heads in the sand and ignore crucial threats or critical capabilities.

The need for a variety of scenarios has already been recognized in some parts of the DoD community. For example, the scenarios underlying the JFCOM series of experiments leading up to Millennium Challenge '02 (Unified Vision '01 and Limited Objective Experiments) were crafted as a series of vignettes that move from a serious international situation where the U.S. has clear interests and a range of tools can be used to shape the environment, through a crisis phase requiring working with other governments in military planning and preparations, to a military actions phase, followed by a conflict termination and regional restoration problem. Similarly, the visualization tool experiments performed within DARPA's CPOF Program used both tactical military force-on-force scenarios and an insurgency situation where the U.S. role was limited to protecting U.S. forces, personnel, and facilities as well as assisting a host government in dealing with the insurgency. Not surprisingly, these experiments showed that new tools and different mindsets were needed across the different types of missions examined.

Selecting the "Interesting Range"

Each transformation experiment or experimentation campaign should be aimed at some interesting "range" in the available scenario space. Since the relevant scenarios will have to both focus attention on the set of variables of interest and also provide a rich enough environment to allow variations and behaviors that have not been foreseen (or fully foreseen), considerable effort is often required to select the appropriate set of scenarios and vignettes. For example, the threat and mission space defined in Figure 8-1 is probably a good starting point for selecting the strategic and operational context(s) that a given experiment will cover. Once that broad parameter space has been chosen, however; the specific actors (red, blue, and neutral), operating environment (terrain, weather, and relevant political, social, and cultural contexts), and the driving events that will ensure that the experiment is properly focused must also be articulated.

The initial CPOF visualization experiments provide a good example. The Program decided that it would focus efforts on two important parts of the mission space (U.S. operations in support of a weaker coalition partner that had been invaded by a more powerful neighbor, and support to a host government faced with an active insurgency), and the experimentation team had to put the other elements of the scenario in place.

For the high-intensity military operation, the geopolitical context was organized around a situation that the U.S. plans for routinely: the invasion of a small country that cannot defeat the aggressor and requests U.S. assistance. Environment and terrain were borrowed from the real world, training centers for which good map data and real weather data were available. However, because situation awareness was one of the experiment variables, the terrain was expanded to include nearby areas and the map was rotated to reduce its familiarity. The friendly and hostile forces were created to represent forces like those the U.S. expects to see. Two very different tactical situations were selected, located on different terrain and involving different missions, force structures, and driving events. These tactical situations had quite different likely futures, threats, and opportunities. The two insurgency scenarios were located in a real world country with a relatively weak government and tradition of democracy. Sanctuary was assumed in a neighboring country. The same force structures were used in both insurgency cases. Two different patterns of driving events were developed, one pointing to a major insurgent offensive and the other to "business as usual" rather than any radical initiative by the rebels. Since the purpose of the experiment was to find out which types of visualizations give better situation awareness (more correct, more complete, more focused on specific threats/opportunities and actions), this variety in missions, contexts, actors, and driving contexts yielded a rich and useful set of scenarios focused on the subjects' ability to rapidly and correctly comprehend a variety of military situations.

Note that this individual experiment did not (and did not attempt to) cover the entire range of interesting situations. Rather, it selected a range with considerable variety in context and mission type, leaving some other important types of operation (e.g., peace operations) for later experimentation. Given the resources available, taking on more scenarios and treating them in adequate depth would have been very difficult.

How Much Detail?

The depth of detail needed for a transformation experiment depends on the focus of the experiment. Two examples should suffice to make this clear – scenarios for the major JFCOM experimentation venues such as Unified Vision '01 or the Air Force's JEFX) and the scenarios needed for a simple interpersonal experiment in information sharing and shared awareness.

Major experimentation venues involve a variety of echelons (typically a CINC slice to help drive the events, a Joint Task Force headquarters, component commands and operating units), a variety of functions (intelligence, logistics, operations, etc.), consideration of host government and coalition factors, and development over time from pre-crisis to crisis, to military engagement and war termination. These major efforts require a complex reality and the capacity for the participants to use the rich set of sources available in the real world to support their situation awareness and decisionmaking. Today, these involve organic intelligence, national assets, reach back, outreach, and Internet sources. These experimentation venues also demand specific scenario materials to drive the variety of specific discovery, hypothesis testing, and demonstration experiments contained within them. The scenario materials needed for these experimentation venues will typically require a year or more of development time, and a number of person-years of effort. In many cases, they will draw from existing (often approved) scenarios in order to minimize the costs and ensure credibility, though ensuring adequate uncertainty and free play to challenge participants and test key propositions about situation awareness, decisionmaking processes, and synchronization should limit reliance on "canned" scenarios and pre-scripted adversary behaviors.

By contrast, when Thoughtlink sought to research how groups exchange information and collaborate to solve problems, they set up a simple set of scenarios. Every group was given the same problem within a game they call "SCUDHUNT." The problem is to locate Scud missiles in a grid space, very much like the old game of Battleship. However, rather than blind trial and error, each team is given a set of sensors with different properties (ranges, probability of correct detection, probability of false alarms, etc.). Primary decisionmaking is about how to employ the sensors. The behaviors of interest have to do with how the group shares information and reaches conclusions about the locations of the missiles. Dependent variables include the degree to which each group (a) is correct about Scud locations (situation awareness) and (b) agrees on those locations (shared situation awareness). The primary scenario manipulation is simply the locations of the Scuds, which can be handled by a random number generator. The experimentation team can obviously also manipulate the characteristics of the sensors, the size of the grid to be searched, the number of missiles present, the types of subjects, and the communications systems available to them, but these are controls in the experiment, not scenarios. Note that this set of experiments is designed to learn about human behavior, so the lack of richness in the scenarios does not impact the experiment itself.

Hence, the level of detail needed for an experiment clearly depends on the purpose of the experiment. Scenarios can be very rich and therefore very difficult and expensive to develop and support. However, since they are not ends in themselves, scenarios should be limited investments designed only to facilitate the larger experimentation process. Indeed, scenarios will almost always be incomplete, and some detail of interest and value to the subjects will not have been considered when the scenarios were built. In these cases the value of agile, resourceful experimentation teams, including those in the "white" or control cell and the experiment support team will be demonstrated. Smart teams rely on these resources rather than attempting to foresee any and all possible issues and questions.

Driving Data Collection and Analysis

Scenarios must drive the data collection process and ensure that enough data are taken on key issues to support the data analysis plan. Empirical data require appropriate stimuli. For example, if a research issue is the speed with which information can be transmitted throughout a force, the scenario needs to have events in it that should be sent immediately to all force elements. These are relatively rare events in the real world. They include notification that a war has started, reporting the presence of chemical, biological, or radiological weapons in the battlespace, virus alerts and notifications of other types of electronic attacks, and notification of termination of hostilities. Hence, scenarios where this is an issue would need to have appropriate stimuli built in at intervals that permit testing of the speed of information distribution.

Analyses of exercises have shown that standard training exercises involve about 50 important force-wide decisions per week, based on several hundred "understandings" or integrated situation assessment conclusions, and tens of thousands of reports about friendly, adversary, or environmental developments. Scenarios designed to focus on decisionmaking will need to force the pace of decisions to generate a large enough number to support analysis. Scenarios intended to illuminate issues about situation awareness will need to make enough changes in the situation to permit capture of enough meaningfully different observations and the time delay involved in noticing and processing such changes.

Adequate variety is also needed in the location where scenarios deliver stimuli. For example, functional distribution is essential if situation awareness and decisionmaking are to be assessed across operations, intelligence, and logistics. Similarly, all elements of the experimentation command will need to be stimulated to report situation changes and make decisions if their activities are to be used in the analysis. A simple, common mistake is to have one element of a force remain in reserve, therefore reducing its role and making it difficult to capture data about its decisionmaking.

Scenario Selection, Adaptation, and Creation

Experimentation teams have their choice of selecting, adapting, or creating scenarios. Which approach they select should depend on the most efficient and effective way to get the job done. The criteria for scenarios include two of those underlying measures of merit – validity and credibility. *Validity* here refers to the ability of the scenario to correctly represent all the factors and relationships in the conceptual model underlying the experiment. This is often an issue of adequate richness. *Credibility* (face validity in social science literature) refers to acceptance by the professional communities involved in the experiment – subjects, researchers, and the supported decisionmakers. Richness is a factor here, also, but sensitivity to existing professional knowledge is also important. If these two central criteria can be met with an existing set of scenarios, then they should be used. If existing scenarios can be modified to meet these criteria cost effectively, that is adequate. However, the experimentation team must be ready to create some or all the needed scenarios in order to achieve validity and credibility.

Approved scenarios are often suggested as the solution because they (a) represent major investments and benefit from established expertise, and (b) support modeling and analyses of a variety of issues based on a common set of assumptions and background data. These features make them attractive. However, most approved scenarios are developed by individual Services and lack genuine joint perspectives. They are also vulnerable to the problem of familiarity, meaning subjects' situation awareness and course of action analyses are informed by prior knowledge. Most importantly, however, approved scenarios build on existing organizational structures, communications systems, sensors, and doctrine. Since transformational experimentation is about new systems and new ways of doing business, approved scenarios may be too constrained to adequately support these experiments or experimentation campaigns.

Scenario Selection

Fortunate experimentation teams will be able to select a scenario and use it without change. Formal, approved scenarios do exist, particularly those developed by the Services to support cost effective evaluation of systems. These should be chosen when they offer adequate richness and variety to support the experiment's goals. However, meaningful transformation experimentation cannot be performed on single scenarios, nor on scenarios where adversary behavior is scripted and therefore cannot be impacted by friendly actions. The concepts underlying transformation, such as network-centric operations and effects-based operations, have, as their fundamental rationale, impacting and altering adversary behavior. Hence, scenarios that assume adversary actions and behaviors do not provide an adequate basis for experimenting with them.

Given that uncertainty and the ability to develop shared situation awareness are often crucial elements in military operations, foreknowledge of scenarios will be a threat to the validity of many experiments. Hence, off-the-shelf scenarios may not be appropriate in some situations where their substance is a good fit to the experimentation goals. In such cases, serious consideration should be given to scenario adaptation, which builds on the richness of existing scenarios, but alters key events and actors in ways that create more uncertainty.

One novel development has been the increasing use of commercial games for military experimentation. The logic is that commercial gamers have invested in a variety of simulations at levels ranging from single shooters to battles and campaigns. They have already made a variety of decisions about how to trade off reality with ease of use and have framed a range of open ended decision situations. Use of these games, perhaps with additional instrumentation of the subjects so their behaviors and decisions can be readily recorded and analyzed, saves the costs of scenario adaptation and development. Game costs and equipment costs are also well below those needed for developing and supporting major military simulations.

Scenario Adaptation

Adaptation is sometimes a cost effective way to build on what exists. The goal here is to reuse much of what has already been developed (and hopefully pretested) in another context, but to introduce variety and uncertainty appropriate to the conceptual model.

Adaptation may be needed when existing scenarios are already familiar to the subjects, when the existing scenarios do not include all the factors in the conceptual models, or when the existing scenarios do not allow enough free play.

The simplest adaptations alter the geopolitical context. This can often force the subjects to behave as though they have novel constraints and uncertainties. Altering the relevant actors (new military forces or forces from other countries) can also profoundly impact the situation and subject behavior with a relatively modest investment in scenario adaptation. Simple changes in sensors, fusion processes, and communications structures (often needed to move the experiment from today's context into the future context needed for transformational experimentation) can also alter a scenario significantly. However, care needs to be taken to ensure that the subjects, particularly military subjects, understand what is different from today's capabilities and are given reasons to find those changes reasonable, or at least plausible enough to be worthy of experimentation. Changes in mission type are perhaps the most important because they allow the experiment to explore the interesting space more thoroughly. However, they often involve the greatest level of effort and may save little over developing new sets of scenarios.

Adaptation should, whenever possible, be done collaboratively with those who developed the original scenarios. It should also be reviewed with experts who do not participate in the adaptation process. This is hard, "pick and shovel" work in which every assumption and every detail needs to be made explicit. The most common error is to have the adapted elements of a scenario at a different level of detail (either more shallow or more detailed) than the scenarios being altered. More shallow elements result from being in a hurry or inadequately staffed. More detailed elements result from losing sight of the instrumental role of scenarios.

A final, increasingly important form of adaptation is the development of federations of models that can be used to drive experiments. These federations allow specialized sub-models of key processes, such as command and control or logistics, to run in greater detail than the main model driving the scenario. This allows both distributed processing (greater efficiency) and more valid scenario support (greater detail and variety in key processes). While this remains a challenging technical task (synchronizing the different models is not a trivial problem), it has proven useful for some experiments.

Scenario Creation

When the problem is fundamentally human behaviors and interactions (as in SCUDHUNT), a very simple set of scenarios may be adequate and the costs of developing them can be quite modest. This is the primary context where scenario creation will be the most desirable option. Peer review to ensure that the limited scenarios are adequate to examine the conceptual model of interest is a wise practice, even in these simple cases.

Where complex, realistic military settings are needed most researchers look for tools, such as DARPA's Synthetic Theater of War (STOW), that can integrate large amounts of data about terrain, weather, military forces, and contextual variables such as refugees. However, even these tools require major efforts (multiple person-years) to support new scenarios. These tools also typically build in a variety of interaction and communication patterns that may require considerable effort to identify and change if required. Hence, they are best used when experience and expertise in the particular tool is readily available to the experimentation team.

However, given that transformation is about new and innovative ways of accomplishing military objectives and often involve an asymmetric adversary, they will, at times, require the creation of genuinely new, militarily rich scenarios. These are really simulations that are designed to allow exploration of the conceptual models under study. The expertise and effort required here should not be underestimated. Even with the computational power and bandwidth available today, this process can be expected to take a couple of years on calendar time and several person-years of effort. Expertise in all the relevant domains (command and control, maneuver, fires, logistics, information operations, intelligence, etc,) as well as technical engineering fields (modeling, simulation, databases, information processing, experiment design) and the sciences that underlie that engineering (physics, weather, behavioral sciences, etc.) will all be required. Moreover, the team will need to use a collaborative work process that keeps all of these types of expertise and experience engaged.

As with past efforts at developing new simulations and models, this process can be expected to be so expensive that its products will need to be reusable. That criterion, coupled with the need for adequate uncertainty and free play to allow exploration of new concepts and behaviors, means that such a simulation would ideally be built as a shell that can rapidly and easily be fed new material (C2 structures, doctrines, terrain, missions, etc.). The key here is rapidity. The tool for scenario generation and support will need to be modular and flexible. At the same time, that simulation will need, in its first instantiation, to fully represent the experiment it is designed to support, both in terms of containing all the elements of its conceptual model and in terms of the depth need to support questions from and actions by experimentation subjects. At this writing, agent-based models appear to be an attractive alternative, but their ultimate value has not been established.

Example Application: Self-Synchronization Experiment

Some decisions made in earlier phases constrained the self-synchronization experiment. For example, the team had decided that this experiment would focus on warfighting and include only close allies. In addition, because self-synchronization implies both cross-echelon and cross-functional activities, the scenarios needed involve multiple levels of command and more than one function.

Examination of existing scenarios showed that they all assume current doctrine and organizational factors, which ruled them out as a basis for a self-synchronization experiment. Even adapting one of them was seen as requiring a massive effort, perhaps more than beginning from scratch.

Fortunately, a commercial game had just come on the market that used the typography and forces of the NATO Kosovo campaign, but did not have the political restrictions that limited the early NATO actions. The commercial game also allowed customized changes in organizations, sensors, and communications systems and was designed for multiple players on the Internet. A limited license was purchased for government use and the gamers who had developed the commercial system were retained as consultants to help install the game on a network that could be used for classified applications.

The geopolitical context was changed so that NATO's objective was to first deter war crimes and, if necessary, to defeat hostile forces and occupy the territory of Kosovo. Russia, whose presence and actions contributed uncertainty in the real Kosovo situation, was left in its original role and played by members of the control cell. Because of the flexibility of the game, red forces (which included regular forces and militias) could undertake different missions and respond differently to NATO initiatives. All game runs were started with identical situations, as were the pretests and training sessions.

However, the subjects were warned that the game might take different patterns depending on red's objectives and opportunities. Red was given a set of five alternative objectives:

- Offer conventional battle;

- Retreat to difficult terrain and operate as guerrillas;

- Retreat to urban areas and use the civilian populations as shields and barriers;

- Seek to divide Kosovo into two regions so the northern region would become a part of Bosnia, the southern could become independent, but would be impoverished; and

- Conduct scorched earth operations while retreating across the province.

These alternative objectives were randomly assigned to the experiment trials with the rule that no team of subjects would encounter the same set of red objectives twice.

Blue capabilities were advanced to the year 2010, particularly in terms of sensors and communications systems. Blue commanders were encouraged, but not forced, to develop joint mission forces rather than rely on traditional component led force elements. Logistics and logistic constraints used real terrain, but lift power from the 2010 timeframe.

Forces on both sides were fixed, as were NATO objectives. This, plus the reuse of terrain in all scenarios, led the experimentation team to expect learning over time by the subjects, so a statistical test for improved performance across trials was required in the data analysis plan.

Conclusion

No single scenario is likely to support meaningful transformational experimentation. However, scenarios are not ends in themselves. Rather, they are part of the effort necessary for successful experiments. They should be chosen or developed to represent an interesting and important part of the problem space under study. The criteria for good scenarios are that they are valid (cover all the elements of the conceptual model underlying the experiment richly enough to support the necessary analysis) and credible to all those participating and using the results of the experiment. The scenarios needed will also have to be coordinated with the data collection and data analysis plans to ensure that they stimulate an adequate number and variety of activities for a successful experiment.

Scenarios can be adopted, adapted, or created. The approach chosen should be based on cost effectiveness. Selecting an existing scenario because it is inexpensive is wrong if it does not support all the important elements of the problem under study. Adapting existing scenarios will often be attractive. However, the true costs of adaptation can be very high if the mechanisms in which they are built are inflexible. Development of new scenarios is most attractive in simple experiments and least attractive when a realistic military "world" must be built from scratch. Despite the best efforts of the modeling and simulation communities, many of the existing tools lack the flexibility needed for genuinely transformational experimentation. Commercial games may provide attractive, cost effective scenarios for some experiments.

Peer reviewers and consultants familiar with the scenarios and tools being used are important cross-checks on the quality of the work. No scenario should ever be used without a thorough pretest. The ultimate tests for scenarios are validity and credibility. Valid scenarios reflect all of the factors seen as important in the conceptual model. Credible scenarios are acceptable by the research community, the subjects, and the decisionmakers who will be informed by the experiment.

---

[1]This matrix was initially developed by Randy Pherson, a former National Intelligence Officer, and has since been refined by a team from Evidence Based Research working with the Joint Staff and the Decision Support Center in the Office of the Secretary of Defense.

CHAPTER 9

Data Analysis and Collection Plans

Purpose and Focus

B eyond (but interacting with) metrics and scenarios, the experimentation team must complete explicit plans for the collection and analysis of data. These two efforts are always tightly linked because analysis is always limited to that data which has been collected. Moreover, training for collectors must ensure that the data from the experiment are those that the analysts expect and that unplanned differences (anomalies) are clearly identified and recorded so that either (a) the analysis process can be used to compensate for them or (b) the contaminated data can be removed from the analyses. These two plans are vital because they are at the heart of experimentation – ensuring that valid and reliable data are captured and that the analyses undertaken address the key issues in the experiment, as well as that the available data and information are fully understood and exploited, but not misused.

Relationship between the Data Analysis Plan and the Data Collection Plan

Because data collection must be accomplished before data analysis, there is a tendency to think of the data collection plan as being developed first. However, the only purpose of a data collection plan is to feed a data analysis plan. Hence, the work process must begin with positing a data analysis plan – how the research issues will be addressed with the data generated from the experiment. In economic terms, the data analysis plan acts as the source of demand. The data collection plan acts as the source of supply.

Having noted the need to consider the requirements for analysis first, the reality is that practical factors (access, minimizing interference, classification, etc.) may limit what can actually be collected in any given experiment. Hence, while the data analysis plan should be posited first, the process of developing the two plans will be iterative. The initial data requirements from the posited data analysis plan will have to be put into the context of the experiment setting, the collection means available (pre-experiment, automatic, observer based, SME-based, etc.), and the scenarios being used. That process will identify challenges, such as data that are needed or desired but are not available as originally conceptualized. That will typically lead to changes in the analysis plan. In addition, the data collection planning process may identify needs for analyses (for example needs for inter-coder reliability tests) not foreseen in the initial data analysis plan. This iterative process may continue right through the pretest and even be necessary in order to overcome anomalies and obstacles arising during the experiment. However, the fundamental principle driving the process should be clear: the purpose of the data collection plan should be to provide what is needed for the analysis plan. Losing sight of this principle always leads to the same problem of collecting what is easy to collect rather than what is needed for a successful experiment that contributes to the growing body of knowledge.

Finally, the experimentation team needs to remember that neither of these plans is an end in itself. Both are instrumental to the overall experiment goals. As such, they are constrained by, and must fit into, the rest of the experimentation plan. The data collection plan must be coordinated with the scenarios, the pretest, the training plan for collectors, and the systems used to archive data and information. The data analysis plan must be organized for end-to-end application from a thorough debugging in the pretest through post-experiment modeling and analysis.

Data Analysis Plans

Analysis is the processing of learning what you want to know from what you already know or can know. As such, it is a crucial part of any experiment. Experiments are about generating empirical data and information. Organizing experimentation results and integrating them with existing knowledge to generate new and valid knowledge and insights is the analytic challenge.

The data analysis plan takes its shape from the conceptual model underlying the experiment and/ or experimentation campaign. The first step is to identify the dependent variables and their measures, then the active independent variables and their measures, and finally the intervening variables (including those that are to be controlled in the experiment) and their measures. The specific measures are important because they provide information about the level of measurement (nominal, ordinal, interval, or ratio) available on each variable of interest. Those levels of measurement, in turn, help to determine the appropriate analytic techniques to be applied.

The other key factors needed to select the appropriate analytic techniques are the numbers of observations or independent data points expected for each variable. The use of parametric techniques, for example, assumes that enough independent observations will be available in each experiment trial to make their use appropriate. Where fewer observations are likely to be available, or the assumption of independence cannot be made properly, non-parametric analyses may be more appropriate.

Analysis is typically organized into three phases:

- Descriptive analyses of individual variables;

- Bivariate analysis of relationships; and

• Multivariate analyses of larger patterns.

These three phases build on one another to provide a comprehensive understanding of what has (and has not) been learned in the experiment.

Descriptive Analysis of Individual Variables

Assuming that the data collection effort has ended with the tasks of data reduction (converting raw data and information into the form required for analysis) and data assembly (creation of an integrated data set, including meta-data that data pedigrees are intact), the first real analytic effort is descriptive analysis of each variable of interest (univariate analyses). These descriptive analyses are performed to (a) identify and correct data anomalies, (b) understand the distribution of each variable, and (c) identify any transformations of those variables with distributions that may make analysis misleading.

Identification (and correction) of data anomalies is simply a search for those data that appear to be incorrect on the surface. For example, if data from a nominal category (such as the military service of a subject) with valid codes of 1 through 4 is found to contain a value of 7, the value is clearly incorrect. Similarly, if the years of service (ratio variable) is found to contain an entry of 77 (which is logically possible, but highly unlikely to be correct), some form of error is the likely cause. Having found these anomalous values, the analysis plan will provide the time and effort necessary to research them in the original records and find the correct values. Since all data will have been processed by humans, including such common problem sources as keystroke errors (about 2 percent for unchecked entries), anomalies are likely to be found in any large data set.

Those data items that are clearly anomalous and cannot be corrected will need to be excluded from subsequent analyses. In any case, the descriptive statistics will need to be rerun after all the anomalies have been identified and corrected or removed.

The distributions of each variable will be examined once the anomalies have been removed. These reviews are a search for variables that may be distributed in ways that can cause errors in analysis. In a common example, one or more variables may be "invariant" (have only a single value) or nearly so (have only a small number of cases that differ from a single value). Those variables should be removed from the analysis since they cannot contribute to differences in the dependent variables of interest. (Of course, an invariant or nearly invariant dependent variable indicates that the experiment did not manipulate that variable and cannot generate insight or knowledge about its causes.) Invariant or nearly invariant factors are essentially assumptions of the cases studied and should be noted as such in the analysis and write-up of the experiment. If they are potentially important in the underlying conceptual model, they will need to be included in subsequent experiments.

The most common such problem is the discovery of a small number of outliers (cases that are very distant from the bulk of the data). These cases will make the application of simple linear statistics, such as Pearson correlations or linear regression, misleading. They can often be handled by transforming the variable (for example, using a log conversion that preserves the order of the cases but reduces the effect of the distance between observations) or by creating a new variable that excludes the outlying cases (this loses information by excluding some cases that are clearly different from the main set, but preserves the information from the bulk of the cases) or creating a new (dummy) variable that subdivides the cases into the outliers and the main cases. Obviously, this last transformation would also involve examining the outlying cases in an effort to identify what differentiates this subset from the rest of the data.

This last technique is really a recognition by the analytic team that the descriptive analysis suggests a bimodal distribution. Examination of the distributions is a crucial step since many analytic techniques assume an underlying distribution in the data. For example, linear regression assumes that the data are drawn from a single population that forms a "normal" distribution characterized by homoscedasticity (the variance is constant across the range), which may not be true of the data on some variables in a particular experiment. Finding that the distributions of some variables do not meet the assumptions of some particular analytic techniques may cause the analysis team to select new techniques or to run more cross-checks (add analyses or techniques to the original set). That level of detail is beyond this Code of Best Practice, except to note that statistical expertise is one of the disciplines that should be available to any experimentation team.

When the univariate analyses are complete, the data should be ready to support more sophisticated analyses and the experimentation team should understand its basic properties (ranges, central tendency, dispersion, distribution) richly. This knowledge is a crucial element in performing intelligent analyses later and interpreting the analyses well.

Bivariate Analyses of Relationships

While the conceptual model for almost any interesting transformational experiment will be multivariate, jumping directly to multivariate techniques will often lead to missing interesting and important dynamics within the data. Since experimentation is a process of learning, skipping over the bivariate relationship is inconsistent with the goals of the effort. Moreover, most of the hypotheses that are offered will be stated in bivariate terms within the model (IF A, THEN B, under CONDITION C). These bivariate relationships form the bulk of the testable propositions under analysis.

There is one exception to this best practice. On rare occasions, most likely during discovery experimentation, a team will be dealing with a very large number of variables in a knowledge domain that has not been well-researched or explored. In these cases, the best practice is to apply inductive techniques such as factor analysis or multi-dimensional scaling in order to establish the data structure. This topic is discussed in somewhat more detail in the section discussing multivariate techniques. However, in no case should the analytic team rush into this type of exploratory analysis before the univariate, descriptive analyses have been completed.

The task of examining bivariate relationships will typically proceed from the simplest techniques (scatter plots to look for visual patterns) to algorithmic-based analyses (Chi Square and Peterson correlations, for example). Moreover, the properties of the data (nominal, ordinal, etc.), number of observations available, and variable distributions will combine to indicate the appropriate techniques. These choices should be made by the statistically knowledgeable members of the experimentation team and subject to change or adjustment when the descriptive, univariate analyses are performed.

There is a natural order to the bivariate analyses. With current analytic tools, there is no practical barrier to running "all against all" bivariate analyses. However, generating massive amounts of computer output is very likely to overwhelm the analytic team and make the process of digesting and interpreting the analysis (learning what you want to know) much slower and more difficult than is necessary. Moreover, the seductive approach to "knowing everything all at once" will also lead to the temptation to select a single set of tools (for example, Pearson correlations) as though all the variables have the same properties and distributions. The purpose of the bivariate analyses is to simplify the problem – reducing the number of variables that must be included and focusing on the data regions where useful results are most likely to be found. Hence, the best practice is to decompose the bivariate search for relationships into manageable subsets and perform them in a structured order.

In order to identify the relationships between the various factors and variables, the order for conducting bivariate analyses is:

1. Dependent variables;

2. Control factors;

3. Control factors and dependent variables;

4. Independent variables;

5. Control factors and independent variables; and

6. Independent variables and dependent variables.

The logic behind this order is simple. First, dependent variables are supposed to be independent of one another. If they are confounded (tend to move together across the cases), then they will be associated with the same causal factors (sets of independent and control variables). Strongly correlated dependent variables (sharing half or more of their variance) are essentially the same phenomenon and need not be analyzed independently. They will turn out to have the same or very similar causes. Two actions are implied when strong correlations are found between two dependent variables: (a) select one of them for full analysis (thus saving considerable effort) and (b) revisit the underlying conceptual model because it incorrectly distinguishes between two factors that are closely associated.

Those dependent variables with modest (but significant) levels of bivariate correlation should be kept in the analysis, but they should be analyzed separately. As the analytic process proceeds, these relationships are likely to emerge as important in building a comprehensive model, suggesting redefinition of the variables, merging them because they are different ways of describing the same phenomenon, or splitting them because they reveal the importance of some third causal factor or underlying condition.

Bivariate relationships between the control factors should be determined early in the process because discovering strong associations will save time and energy later. If control factors are confounded, one or more of them can be removed from the analysis. If they have significant association with one another, they may later be found to merge, split, or need redefinition.

Examining the relationships between control factors and the dependent variables is a simple, early cross-check on the effectiveness of the research design. The research design is intended to exclude causal patterns driven by the control factors. For example, in an experiment involving many subjects, subject experience would typically be designed out of the experiment by random assignment of subjects. If, however, analysis showed that subject experience was related to performance on one or more dependent variables, the analytic team would know that the design had been unsuccessful and the experience factor would need to be included in the later multivariate analyses and considered in the process of refining the conceptual model. More typically, the bivariate analysis of relationships between the control factors and the dependent variables simply validates the fact that the experiment design worked and that the control factors have no direct causal impact on the data from the experiment.

One major exception that can be expected in many human subject experiments is *learning* over time and across trials. Despite the range of tools and techniques used to ensure that subjects have mastered the experimental technologies, that they have established teams and work processes, and that the tasks assigned to subjects are equally challenging, human subjects may still learn and improve performance over time and trials. Hence, the propositions that time and trial are related to performance must be examined in every human experiment (as well as machine experiments where efforts have been made to create learning systems). If significant bivariate patterns are found, their shape and parameters will be needed in order to apply statistical controls in the later, multivariate analyses.

Examination of bivariate relationships among independent variables is important because they are assumed, in most analytic tools, to be unrelated. If they are associated with one another, then analyses involving that pair of variables will be confounded – the same variation in a dependent variable will be "explained" by more than one independent variable. This will yield a statistical explanation that is false; it will look artificially strong.

The same approaches already articulated must be used when meaningful bivariate association is found between independent variables – merging, splitting, or removal from the analysis. In addition, when the pattern of association suggests that several independent variables are linked, one of them can be selected as a "marker" variable for the cluster. However, this marker variable should be understood to represent the entire cluster, not just the specific phenomenon it measures. Decisions on merging, splitting, removing, or selecting representative variables will depend on examining the bivariate scatter plots and considering the strength of the association present. They should also be examined for implications for the conceptual model underlying the experiment. Patterns of association between independent variables imply that some distinctions made in that model have not been strong enough to show up in the experiment data.

Bivariate associations between independent and control factors are also signs that the conceptual model or the research design may be flawed. For example, if a control factor was intended to ensure that two subsets of scores on independent variables were examined in the experiment, but an association was found between them, the multivariate analysis would need to be informed by that fact. If, for example, "hasty decisionmaking" is distinguished from "deliberate decisionmaking" as an intervening variable expected to separate two different types of decision processes, but deliberate decisionmaking was found to be associated with early trials and hasty decisionmaking with later trials, the research design would have failed to keep the control variable "trial" from being confounded with the variables about decision type. This does not destroy the validity or utility of the experiment data, but it does mean that these factors will all need to be considered together in the multivariate analyses and that it may not be possible to distinguish the effect of "trial" (which is likely to reflect learning within the experiment) from the type of decisionmaking process followed.

Finally, with all this prior knowledge in mind, the analytic team will examine the direct, bivariate hypotheses between the independent and dependent variables. These are true tests of the strength of association for the direct propositions of hypotheses posited in the conceptual model. However, they go beyond those propositions in two important ways. First, all possible bivariate pairs are tested in order to allow the analysis team to consider the possibility that the conceptual model is not perfect – there may be significant empirical relationships that were not originally considered likely. This is most likely to be true in early experimentation in a domain. Second, some of the bivariate relationships being explored will already be understood to be confounded in that other strong patterns of association have been identified earlier in the analysis. In these cases, the analytic team already has insight into some of the multivariate relationships that will be found when the data have been fully examined.

Multivariate Analyses

Multivariate analyses are the effort to examine the experimentation data as a system. The tools and techniques applied will vary with the number of variables being examined, the properties of those variables, the number of independent observations available for the analysis, and the state of the art knowledge in the arena under study.

Classic techniques for experimentation are the ones that look for simple explanations of the dependent variables. Analysis of variance, multiple regression, and discriminant function analysis (where an ordinal dependent variable is being explained) are the most common tools. They have emerged as common practice because they permit the user to select different subsets of data and compare their explanatory power, provide information about the degree to which variance in the dependent variable is explained, and also indicate the contribution of each independent or control variable to that explanation.

As noted earlier, some experiments will generate a large number of variables in knowledge domains where little prior work has been done and the underlying structure of the problem is not well-understood. In these cases, the data analysis plan may well include tools that are inherently deductive such as factor analysis or multidimensional scaling.

This type of analysis is tricky because the tools search for clusters of variables on a purely statistical basis. Hence, the analytic team will need to examine the clusters carefully and label them in ways that reflect their rich contents, but do not oversimplify the patterns observed. For example, the dependent variables can "load" anywhere in the data structure. If they cluster together, they may be confounded. If, however, they each load on a different cluster, then the other variables in those clusters will tend to indicate the set of causes relevant to each dependent variable. If, however, one or more of the dependent variables remain distant from any of the identified clusters, the data is unlikely to provide a statistically sound explanation for them.

Another type of inductive analysis that might be considered is the development of a learning model using techniques like neural networks. These tools build an explanation by finding efficient paths through sets of cases. They can be helpful in creating new insights into poorly understood domains. However, they do not generally provide the statistical insight necessary to weight factors or the knowledge structure needed to sort out the roles of intervening variables from independent variables. As with the clustering techniques, neural nets also require very careful interpretation because they are not based on a theoretical structure (other than the selection of the set of variables to be included) and therefore can generate explanations with little or no validity.

The results of applying inductive techniques should not, generally, be the last step in the multivariate analysis of any experiment. These results tend to be suggestive rather than definitive. Consequently, they are most properly used as a way to find underlying patterns or structures in the knowledge domain. Armed with this information, the analytic team will then be able to use more traditional techniques to generate an efficient explanation that can be used to assess the propositions or hypotheses under examination. In some cases, the inductive tools will suggest very different sets of hypotheses and require major revision of the underlying conceptual model. Where the experiment is in a knowledge domain with little prior work, this may indicate a genuine breakthrough. However, where substantial prior work exists, a careful examination of the emergent (new) model is best practice. In such cases, the experiment is more likely to have explored a unique subset of the phenomenon under study, rather than to have found a genuinely revolutionary causal pattern. In any case, the more traditional analysis should demonstrate the relative strength of the evidence for the new pattern versus the existing relevant literature.

Linkages from the Data Analysis Plan

The data analysis plan should be consciously linked to three other elements of the experiment. First and foremost, it needs to be linked to the data collection plan. That mechanism is used to ensure that the data required for analysis are generated, captured, and organized for analysis. It is the filter through which the scenarios, subjects, and experimentation environment are organized to ensure that the analytic plan can be supported. Changes in the experiment that alter the availability of data will appear as changes in the data collection plan and its outputs. They will need to be fed back into the data analysis plan iteratively to ensure the integrity of the experiment.

The data analysis plan will also be linked to any plan for post-experiment modeling, whether designed as sensitivity analyses or as ways to extrapolate from the experiment to larger areas of application. The results of the analyses become drivers for such models, providing both the relevant scope of those efforts (identifying variables for inclusion and specifying the ranges across which they should be explored) and also providing empirical parameters for those models. Post-experiment modeling may also generate new data streams that can be productively fed back into the overall analysis to broaden its reach or strengthen its findings.

Finally, the data analysis plan will result in the material necessary to revisit, revise, and perhaps extend the conceptual model underlying the experiment. This is the crucial, final step in the analytic process. The statistical results are not an end in themselves. The goal of the experiment is always better knowledge in the domain under analysis. The explicit revision of that model and articulation of the strength of the evidence underlying it is the final analytic step. This translation of the analysis into findings that are clearly articulated, including statements about the degree of uncertainty remaining and other research that should be undertaken, is the final step in analysis. Time and effort for this task must be built into the data analysis plan.

Data Collection Plans

As noted earlier, the data collection plan includes all the variables to be collected, all the places where they are to be collected, all the means of collection, and all the places the data will be stored for processing. This needs to be a major document, incorporating both the broad philosophy being used and also the details necessary for implementation. High quality data collection plans also specify the support required, the training needed, the proficiency standards to be met, the approach to quality control, how the data will be archived to ensure its integrity, and the processes by which data sets will be reduced from their raw form to create the variable sets envisioned by the data analysis plan and assembled for efficient analysis. While it is a major document, this plan is not an end in itself, but rather a means to ensure the data collection process is organized for success and understood by all those who need to support the effort.

Creation of a data collection plan can be thought of as a sequential task, although it will prove to be an iterative one because it is closely linked to the goals of the experiment, the data collection plan, the scenario, the physical spaces available for the experiment, the systems being employed to support the experiment, the subjects, and a host of other factors that are likely to change from the initial concept stage through the pretest phase.

The key "steps" include:

- Specifying the variables to be collected;

- Identifying the collection mechanism for each variable;

- Ensuring access for collecting each variable;

- Specifying the number of observations needed for each variable and checking to ensure they are expected to be generated;

- Identifying the training required to ensure quality data collection;

- Specifying the mechanisms to ensure data capture and archiving; and

- Defining the processes needed for data reduction and assembly.

However, this work sequence is only one key perspective. Looking at data collection plans through the lens of the different types of collection mechanisms that can be employed may yield a more practical and useful set of insights. The types of collection mechanisms used in typical experiments include:

- Automated collection;

- Recording for later reduction;

- Surveys;

- Subject testing; and

- Human observation.

Each of these approaches has particular uses, strengths, weaknesses, and factors that need to be considered when they are employed.

Automated Collection

Automated collection has become more and more important as the information systems have become more and more fundamental to military functions. C4ISR (command, control, communications, computers, intelligence, surveillance, and reconnaissance) functions in particular are increasingly automated and supported by automated systems. As military functions become automated, they are increasingly easy to monitor, but only if plans and preparations are made to capture all of the needed data.

Planning for automated collection requires expertise in the systems being used as well as the variables to be collected. Typical collection foci include system load, workstation load, availability (system, application, and workstation), and usage (system, application, and workstation), as well as capture and comparison of "ground truth" with what is available within the systems and from the individuals (their perceptions and situational awareness).

The tasks that need planning include when and where these items will be captured, how that can be done without impacting the functionality of the systems (either the operator's systems or those being used to drive the experiment), how the clocks on all these different data capture efforts will be synchronized to facilitate comparisons and analyses, how the meta-data tags will be attached to facilitate data reduction and analysis, and where the data will be archived. Because data capture is best done within the systems and federations of systems being used, the earlier these requirements are identified, the better.

Finally, someone on the experimentation team needs to be assigned as the leader to work with the systems analysts and programmers to ensure that they understand the plan and that they have the time and resources needed to support the experiment. A milestone plan, built into the engineering plan needed to bring together all the necessary systems to support the experiment, is best practice and will help ensure that the automated data capture process is a successful effort.

Recording for Later Data Reduction

Experimentation teams worry about their collection processes intruding and causing different behaviors or results. Moreover, human observers are not always available in enough numbers (or are not physically able) to be everywhere. Finally, human observers are able to abstract only a certain level of meaning or amount of data – they must choose what to pay attention to and what to record. As a result, experimenters often prefer to capture verbatim recordings (audio or visual). At this writing (2002), collaborations are becoming an important element in military work processes and have proven difficult to monitor effectively, so they are often recorded for later analysis.

This approach is not a panacea – even the best recording setups do not capture all of the nuances of communications in a command center or military operation. Moreover, recordings often require massive amounts of time and effort to review and reduce to data that can be analyzed. Finally, some past efforts have been plagued by the difficulty of capturing everything, resulting in capturing only one side of some conversations, people stepping out of range of cameras and microphones when they are making decisions, and technical problems with the recording equipment itself.

Experimentation teams engaged in recording need to plan very carefully and ensure that the systems are both fully pretested and also backed up robustly. Key decisions include:

- Whether audio recordings will suffice or video is needed;

- Whether to record everything or only selected materials (including decisions about sampling);

- Creating meta-data to tag the recordings, including how individuals will be identified, including their roles;

- Introducing the topic of recording to the subjects, obtaining appropriate permissions and ensuring privacy protection;

- Positioning and testing the recording equipment;

- Provisioning for equipment failures (backup, anomaly recording, etc.);

- Training those operating the system and archiving the products;

- Ttraining and testing those responsible for data reduction and coding (discussed in more detail in the section below on human observers); and

- Ensuring adequate facilities and time for data reduction and archiving.

Unless these efforts are properly planned, experimenters will find themselves with incomplete or incomprehensible materials or mounds of material they cannot process. This area is one where appropriate expertise on the team and thorough pretesting (both of collection and data reduction) are essential for success.

Surveys

Survey instruments are popular tools because they allow the experimentation team to collect data in a form that is easy to review. They are used in several different ways in transformational experiments. First, they can be used to gather data about the subjects' backgrounds and experience. This is typically done before the experiment (perhaps as part of subject selection) or as an early part of the process used to introduce the subjects to the experiment. The earlier this is accomplished, the easier it will be for the experimentation team to use the data to assign subjects to teams and treatments and to create a data file so that the attributes of the subjects can be used as part of the analysis effort. Subjects are also often surveyed during the experiment to gather their perceptions of the systems and processes they are employing, their knowledge of and attitudes toward other subjects or teams of subjects, their perceptions and insights about the substance of the experiment (for example, their situation awareness), and their ideas about how the systems and work processes might be improved.

Others on the experimentation team are also surveyed in many transformation efforts. Subject matter experts and controllers, for example, often record their perceptions and insights about how the subjects are performing and how the systems and processes they are employing (a) are working and (b) can be improved. Those supporting the experiment (systems analysts, researcher leaders, etc.) are also surveyed to take advantage of their perspectives. Finally, observers may be asked to use survey formats to report what they are seeing.

Surveys can be a "tender trap" in several ways, so they require careful development, pre-test, and monitoring. First, any survey tends to skew the agenda to focus attention on the items included. Hence, it is best practice to include some open-ended items at the end that ask for reflection (for example, "Are there important topics we have failed to ask you about?"). Second, surveys demand time. Planning for the experiment needs to make certain that all respondents are given adequate time to complete the surveys properly. The time required can only be estimated realistically by using pretests in which the respondents are as similar to those being used in the experiment as possible. (The classic error here is to have members of the experimentation team, who are familiar with the issues and understand what is meant by each of the questions "stand-in" for the subjects.)

Surveys must also be pretested because the wording of each item is important and will be subject to interpretation or misunderstanding. Poorly worded or ambiguous questions will not result in quality data. At the same time, in order to accumulate knowledge across experiments, every effort should be made to identify and use common questions. Expertise in questionnaire design is one element needed on teams that plan to use surveys.

Surveys also impact respondent behaviors. For example, a survey that asks respondents to describe the military situation and provides them with a template (What is the key terrain? What are adversary intentions? and so forth) will lead subjects to focus on items that they may have been overlooking in the scenario and to look for those items in later trials. Hence, such structured questions should (a) be chosen to represent "common sense" or training items for the experiment and (b) be introduced to the subjects during their training. Past experience has shown that the "learning behavior" resulting from these structured items can be minimized by ensuring that the subjects are familiar with them before the experiment begins.

Planners should remember that surveys also create work for those doing data reduction and assembly. The more structured the survey data is, the less effort is necessary. For example, simple Lickert scales on which respondents merely check a space or point on a line to indicate their answers provide precise data that can be machine read. Of course, the assumption behind these instruments is that they are not ambiguous and that enough scale points are related to precise statements that different respondents will be able to answer consistently. This can be a subject for the pretest phase. Lickert scales usually need to be labeled at their end points and centers in order to generate consistent responses. For example, an eleven point scale to respond to the question "How much do you believe your team mates trust your judgment?" might have its zero point labeled, "Not At All," its high end point labeled "Completely" and its mid-point labeled, "Somewhat." When surveys are designed and pretested, the data collection plan must include adequate time to complete them as well as adequate time for data reduction and archiving.

Not everyone will need to complete every survey. For small experiments, however, everyone who is involved in relevant activities should be surveyed – the data analysis plan will have to deal with the entire population. For larger efforts, some sampling may be wise, both to reduce the effort needed to process the data and also to ensure that all of the key perspectives are richly represented.

Subject Testing

Subjects may be tested for proficiency or other characteristics. Proficiency tests are used when the results of the experiment are expected to depend, at least in part, on the particular skills of the individuals or teams participating. In other words, if proficiency is a control or is being used to assign subjects in order to control it out of the experiment, testing will be needed. Proficiency tests require pretesting unless they are already established and normalized. Subjects should generally not be told their scores until after the experiment. This prevents a variety of anomalous behaviors (bragging, becoming discouraged, etc.) that can damage the experiment.

Tests for characteristics (IQ, leadership style, etc.) should, if at all possible, be selected from those that have been developed, validated, and normalized on large populations. This is much less work than creating new instruments and procedures, and provides credibility to the work. Planning for these types of tests needs to include having professionals administer them as well as a clear statement to the subjects about what is being assessed, why it is needed, and also how their privacy is being protected. Human subject data needs careful management and should be divorced from the individuals' names throughout its processing. Subject testing also needs to be included in the pretest so that possible problems with introducing the assessments, administering them, and managing the resulting data are all worked out in detail.

Human Observation

Despite progress in automation, many military activities remain human. Hence, whether by reviewing recordings or direct observation, humans will be needed to capture behaviors and interactions at the heart of many experiments. Some of the principles for human observers were discussed in Chapter 5. The discussion here focuses on planning strategies so that those observers will be effective and successful.

Observer selection is a key. They should have both an appropriate substantive background and skills or training as observers. If they are to go on location, they need to "fit in," so they are not a distraction. Observer positioning is a second key issue. The observers must be located where they can gather the material they have been assigned. At the same time, they should be as unobtrusive as possible. Observer training is also crucial. They must have enough training and proficiency testing to ensure that they know what to capture and will be able to capture it reliably. As noted earlier, they should participate in both pretest efforts and the training efforts for the subjects, but all of that should come after they have already mastered their tasks and passed basic proficiency tests. Planners also need to build in redundancy. Extra time must be available for extended training if some of the observers find their tasks difficult. Extra observers also need to be available. They can be assigned quality control roles for the periods when they are not needed. The procedures for establishing and checking inter-coder reliability are also very important. Coders will tend to "drift" as they gain experience and encounter some types of situations more than others will. Cross-checking and (when needed) review training can be used to counter this tendency and maintain the consistency of coding across individuals.

Scheduling is most likely to be problematic for the observers. Early selection is very helpful. Read-ahead material can be used for familiarization and allow better use of face-to-face times. Observers should be organized into teams as early as is practical so that they have an opportunity to work with one another. Time for training and proficiency testing must be generous. Inter-coder reliability tests should be built into the schedule. Shift routines during the experiment should be designed with the fact that observers must be alert. Ideal shifts are 8 hours long, since most observers will have to spend some time organizing, taking transition briefings when they first come on, and debriefing after their shifts. If longer shifts are necessary, physically fit observers must be recruited and strict schedules used to ensure that they get adequate rest. Finally, time for observers to review their notes and create coded data must be generously provided. Failure to do this will mean that the investment in human observers generates results that fall short of the experimentation goals.

CHAPTER 10

Conduct of the Experiment

Purpose

Shakespeare tells us, "There's many a slip twixt cup and lip." Having planned and prepared for the experiment does not guarantee success. The team still needs to pay close attention when the time comes to execute the plan. Just as no military plan survives first contact with the enemy, no experiment plan survives real-world environment and conditions despite the most rigorous planning. One should expect to encounter problems that can adversely impact the quality of the data being collected. This chapter reviews the steps necessary to reap the benefits of the hard work that has gone into conceptualizing and planning transformational experiments.

Pretest

Scope

The pretest should be viewed as a dress rehearsal for all the elements of the experiment. While it will be on a smaller scale and will not involve the same quantities of equipment, subjects, observers, and instrumentation as will be used for the experiment itself, it must be sufficiently robust to exercise all of the relevant procedures and processes. The size, type (discovery, hypothesis testing, or demonstration), and complexity of the experiment will determine the support infrastructure required. This infrastructure will generally include workstations, a simulated environment, communications networks, controllers, observers, technical support personnel, databases, and logistical support. Sufficient time must be provided to fully inspect the systems to ensure that they are operating satisfactorily, not only in a stand-alone mode, but also as a "system of systems." That is, to ensure that they are appropriately interoperable. Additionally, the systems must be tested with the experimental tools running on them. While the number of subjects and the number of test runs will normally be considerably less than for the actual experiment, system tests must stress the system to (or even beyond[1]) the level anticipated for the experiment. There are numerous instances where collaboration experiments failed because the system was satisfactorily tested with n nodes during the pretest, but failed during the experiment where xn nodes were required to operate simultaneously.

In addition to the experimentation infrastructure, elements of the experiment itself need to be tested. This is accomplished by conducting a mini-experiment that mimics the actual experiment. The data collection plan for the pretest should be designed to provide all the same data as that desired for the experiment. The scenario(s) should be the same as those that are to be used during the experiment. This allows the experiment designer to determine whether the required stimuli are provided to the subjects in the manner intended and that they contain those elements necessary to produce the required range of responses from the subjects. The subjects chosen for the pretest should exhibit characteristics similar to the those of the subjects chosen for the experiment. They should have the same levels of expertise and experience. If the experiment subjects are to operate as teams, the subjects for pretest should be similarly organized. The closer the pretest subjects match the experiment subjects, the more the pretest data will be representative of data to be collected during the experiment.

Due to the need for observers/controllers to mimic those for the experiment, their ability to collect the required data and exercise the proper degree of control must be ascertained. Finally, the collected pretest data must be reduced and analyzed as it would be for the experiment. Conducting the pretest in this manner ensures that:

- The subjects are capable of performing their assigned tasks and that they have sufficient time to complete their tasks;

- The observers/controllers can collect and reduce the required data;

- The necessary analyses can be performed on the data; and

- The experiment can be conducted in the allotted time.

Schedule

The pretest should be scheduled sufficiently in advance of the experiment to permit remedial action to be taken. The timing will depend on the size and complexity of the experiment. However, one month would appear to be the minimum time required. Allowing more time than this minimum reduces risk further. This needs to include sufficient time to allow analysis of both the data and the conduct of the pretest. The analysis of the pretest needs to investigate not only what went right and wrong, but also possible remedial actions and their impact on the conduct of the experiment. Finally, there must be time allotted to conduct focused retesting of the areas where remedial action was required.

Training

The pretest also includes a test of the training program. The training program for the pretest (1) provides actual training for the pretest participants and (2) is a trial of the actual training program. The training program, which is discussed in more detail below, should provide answers to three basic questions regarding the experiment:

- Does the training provide the subjects sufficient familiarity with the equipment and exercise procedures that this does not become an issue for analysis (e.g., subjects spent an inordinate amount of time figuring out how to use the equipment)?

- Does the training provide the observers sufficient familiarity with the data collection methodology to allow them to competently collect the required data (observation, recorded data, survey results, etc.)?

- Do the processes specified in the data collection and data analysis plans work so the right data can be captured and the right analyses executed?

Revisions to Detailed Experimentation Plan

Unless this is an experiment like no other, it will be necessary to make revisions to the experiment plan based on what is learned in the pretest. In the majority of cases these will be minor procedure changes that can be accomplished without the need for further testing. However, if the degree of change required is major or if the changes are complex, it may be necessary to conduct a follow-on pilot test that focuses on the revised elements. This is a far better use of resources than attempting the main experiment without a firm idea of how it will unfold or confidence that it will focus on the issues under study.

Pre-Experiment Data Collection

Process

While the main data collection effort occurs during the actual conduct of the experiment, substantial data can be collected before the experiment commences. For those experiments that employ subjects, useful data includes background information such as level of expertise, schools attended, relevant military experience, etc. These data will be used to determine the effect, if any, on the results caused by differences between the subjects' backgrounds. If the experiment analysis plan includes comparisons with past events, baseline data should be assembled and placed in the analytical database prior to the conduct of the experiment. Other data that can be collected includes screen captures for prescripted events, input stimuli, and databases that will not change during the experiment (e.g., friendly and adversary OOB).

Archiving

Unfortunately, as with data collected during the experiment execution, some of the pre-experiment data may be disposed of within a short time after the completion of the experiment. The experiment and its immediate aftermath will be an extremely busy period for the data collection team. It is likely that if pre-experiment data is not archived prior to the experiment, they may become lost in the process. These data should be archived in both their raw and processed forms. The copies placed in the analysis database will be manipulated and are much more likely to be corrupted or destroyed during analysis. Hence, having the original data archived ensures its availability to other research teams and also permits the analytic team for this experiment to go back and verify initial values or initiate novel analyses to explore interesting or important insights.

Data Integrity and Privacy Protection

Data integrity means that not only the reduced data, but also the raw data, should be archived. This allows a link to be made from the raw data to the eventual conclusions and recommendations. Privacy protection is an important element that cannot be overlooked. It is imperative that the subjects understand that they are not being evaluated (the systems, doctrines, organizational innovations, under study are being assessed, not the subjects) and that no links will be made from individual participants to scores and/or results. Not only must they understand this, but they must also be confident that this is true. Failure to instill this confidence can result in distorted results.

Training

Training plays a significant role in the success of an experiment. A well-conceived and executed training program will provide the support team, the observers/controllers, and the subjects with a strong foundation that will enhance their participation in the experiment.

Observers/Controllers

Most data collection/observation goes well beyond simple instrumented collection of data. Command and control experiments generally rely on intelligent data observers/collectors that must apply judgements in collecting and coding the data. It is therefore imperative that they understand why the experiment is being conducted, the underlying theory that explains the hypotheses and metrics, and the context in which the experiment is being conducted. It is therefore absolutely necessary that the observers/controllers have a fundamental understanding of the theory underlying the methodology for confirming or not confirming the hypotheses. This foundation will enable the observers and controllers to make the correct judgements, such as where an observed phenomenon fits into the data collection plan, what data elements are satisfied by this observation, and how the data should be coded. Effective instruction in this area will improve measurement reliability and enhance the construct validity.

The training program should focus on techniques for observation in accordance with the experiment plan regarding how the data is to be collected (observation, survey, questionnaire, instrumentation) and where it is to be collected. The observers/controllers are presented with an overview of the scenario and major events so they know when to expect certain data elements. The program of instruction then focuses on practicing the skills learned during the training program. This is best accomplished by providing vignettes in which the observers/controllers (with guidance) observe situations similar to what they will be exposed to during the experiment and record and code the data. Discussion should follow each vignette with the "school solution" provided. In addition to independent practice, observers/controllers should be present and playing their assigned roles during subject training. This gives them further practical experience and also helps to familiarize the subjects with the experimentation process.

Proficiency tests are used to determine if the observers/controllers have been sufficiently trained to collect the required data. After the lesson portion of the training program, the observers/controllers should be given a proficiency test. The test should include (1) a written exam to test their knowledge of the fundamentals and (2) a practical exam to test their ability to capture and code data correctly. The results of the written exam should be evaluated prior to proceeding with the practical exam. This will ensure that the observers/controllers have mastered the fundamentals of the program. If necessary, a review session should be conducted. For the practical exam, once again the observers/controllers should be placed in vignette situations. This time, however, they will not be receiving guidance, but will be on their own. They will be required to make observations and code the data as if they were observing the actual experiment. Their observations will be evaluated and, again, if necessary, a review session will be conducted.

Peer feedback and teaching one another should be encouraged as these practices help build strong observation teams.

Note that the schedule for the training program needs to have these review sessions built in. Best practice assumes that these sessions will be needed. The price of not reserving time for them can be high, impacting the morale of the participants, the demands placed on the trainers, and the quality of the data collected.

Inter-coder reliability tests are necessary because the evaluation of command and control frequently requires judgements on the part of the observers/controllers. To preserve the integrity of the experiment, it is essential that the observations by different observers result in the same data coded the same way by all data collectors, or, if there are differences that can be controlled for, that statistical controls be employed to mitigate those differences.

Subjects

Many C2 experiments will likely involve comparisons with a current or baseline system using military or ex-military subjects. Unless the subjects are well-trained in the *treatment* system being evaluated, the *baseline* system will have the distinct advantage over a system that is not familiar to the subject. Without proper training, subjects are liable to expend an inordinate amount of energy just mastering the workings of the new system. Subjects who find themselves frustrated by the new systems and processes they are trying to employ will not focus creatively and productively on the substantive tasks they have been assigned.

The subjects will require training on operating the systems, both the underlying infrastructure and the system(s) under consideration. They need to understand how they interface with the system, what tasks it performs, and how it performs them. The subjects also need to understand how the system uses underlying data, what operations it performs on the data to get what results, how it displays the data, and the sources of those data. Training is best accomplished by providing an overview followed by hands-on training. The training should culminate (as with the observers/ controllers) with a proficiency test that demonstrates familiarity with the system. Depending on the complexity of the system(s), hands-on training alone has proven in the past to take a week or more. Not all subjects proceed at the same pace and some may require more time. As noted earlier, perhaps more DoD experiments have failed to achieve their goals because of inadequately trained subjects than for any other single cause.

Whether as part of a team or as a single player, each of the subjects will be playing a role. As such, the subjects need to understand the duties and functions associated with their roles. They also need to understand the processes they are to follow in performing their tasks. Training for roles and processes should also incorporate dry runs using the systems and infrastructure employed in the experiment.

If the training described above were to be carried out sequentially, the training program would be unacceptably lengthy, not to mention disjointed. An integrated, synchronized training program is required to ensure that the parts fit together. The experiment director must ensure that the infrastructure and systems are operating for the training to proceed. Initial training of observers and the training of the subjects should proceed simultaneously and separately. Once the experiment director is satisfied that the observers and subjects are ready, the final segment of the training can proceed. In this segment, the subjects run through a vignette with the observers/collectors taking data. This will give the observers/collectors a feel for how events will unfold during the experiment and uncover any areas of the training requiring further emphasis.

Working with Observers and Controllers

Observers/controllers can make or break an experiment. Adequate training does not ensure success. Attention needs to be paid to how observers/controllers are employed and managed.

Non-interference

Observers generally perform one of two roles. They are either silent observers recording what is happening or they administer questionnaires and/or surveys. In either case, they should not engage participants in conversation, offer opinions, or in any way interfere with the conduct of the experiment. If asked questions, they should answer only to the extent of explaining what it is they are doing, explaining why they are there, or clarifying questions for the subjects. Only if they are dual-acting in the role of controllers may they answer substantive questions or offer items of substance concerning experiment conduct.

Shift Planning

Unlike machines, observers become fatigued. An 8-hour shift with suitable breaks is close to the limit that an observer can remain on station while producing acceptable data. If the experiment is to run longer (e.g., 24 hours per day), shifts will have to be planned. This will require building in time for shift hand-off which needs to be planned so that data is not lost during the hand-off. Observer shift planning should be on a different schedule from the shift changes of the experiment's subjects. This enables observers to observe the shift change processes and information exchanges among the subjects.

Coverage Philosophy

Deciding what data to collect and analyze generally involves tradeoffs between cost and resources, and how comprehensive one needs the effort to be. If the experiment involves observation of single subjects conducting multiple runs at a small number of stations, the data collection can be very comprehensive with one observer at each station being able to observe all that goes on. Observing groups interacting with other groups, or a large-scale event involving large numbers of participants, however, is much more demanding. In these cases, the resources necessary to cover every subject and every interaction are prohibitively expensive. Even if the data could be captured through instrumentation, the resources required for data reduction and analysis could prove unrealistically demanding.

Therefore, decisions on how observers are allocated to subjects/tasks need to be based on what data are necessary to collect in order to achieve the experiment objectives. This may include decisions to sample some kinds of data or to favor collection of some types over others. This will all be part of the data collection plan. However, the observers will need to know what their observations should comprise in great detail. If this is not clear, they may drown in data and miss crucial data because they are focused on relatively unimportant, but easily collected items. Sampling should be considered when too much data is likely to be generated. Building properly instrumented sampling strategies requires expertise and experience.

Supervision

Data collectors require constant supervision. For single subject experiments it will only be necessary to check that all the equipment is being operated (audio and video recorders), that the time schedule is being followed, and the requisite questions are asked and the answers recorded. For larger experiments where the subjects are interacting with each other and with the scenario, checks need to be made to establish that the observations are producing the required data. Refresher training may be required on the fly or during off-hours for observers/collectors who have forgotten the definitions of some of the measures or the importance of collecting certain data. Data sheets must be checked for completeness and for confidence that the correct data are being captured. Data collectors also need to be apprised (in a way that does not alert the subjects) when events are likely to affect their stations. Quite likely, daily or shift meetings will be necessary to keep all the observers/controllers in the loop and the data quality high. This can be difficult to accomplish during 24 hour per day operations, but the price of ignoring the need for team building and timely interaction can be very high.

Data Collection

Automated Collection

With the increasing use of automated systems, much of the data can be collected directly from the system via screen captures, e-mail archiving, requests for information, snapshots of databases, etc. This data must be checked at regular intervals to ensure that the agreed upon data is provided in the proper format. The intervals will be based on the volume of data expected with shorter intervals for higher volumes of data so as not to overwhelm the checking process. Also, care must be taken when creating such a system so that the volume of data does not overload the analysts. Data collected in this manner needs to be carefully selected and archived so that the analysts can readily manipulate it without having to first sort through a mass of raw data. Surveys can also be self-administered in this manner. The subjects can input their own answers into a database for later analysis.

Quality Control

This is perhaps the most important and most overlooked part of data collection. It is tempting to feel that once the data collectors have been trained and briefed, the data collection will be automatic and the next event will be analysis. This couldn't be further from the truth. Automated collection systems and instrumentation can fail, humans bring their own backgrounds and foibles to the program and, regardless of training, some will try to collect what they feel is interesting rather than what they are assigned to collect. To ensure the success of the experiment, it is imperative that data collectors be supervised and a quality control mechanism is in place to ensure that the necessary data is being collected. Those responsible for quality control must ensure that all members of the team, including observers/controllers, are neutral observers and do not influence subjects' answers and/or comments. For example, they must not provide hints to subjects who appear puzzled by a question, or suggest that they consider something that has obviously been overlooked in their analysis. Maintaining the integrity of the data is one of the most important elements of the quality control process.

Incidents will occur where failure to provide certain information could cause the experiment to go drastically awry. To account for those instances, procedures should be established for the observers/ controllers to get advice from the senior member of the observation team who, in turn, should confer with the experiment director and senior controller. On the other hand, the observers need to be alert for qualitative data that can shed light on a situation. The fact that an error of omission has occurred may be very important to understanding subject behavior and decisionmaking, so those cases should be recorded and reported. Another situation that arises is when a supervisor or other trusted agent alerts observers to an event that requires observation. This must be done discreetly. If it is not, the fact that the observer is being alerted will also be an alert for the subject(s).

Management of Anomalies

At the most general level, all experiments are subject to anomalies – system crashes or failures, humans who drop out, and compromises of the scenario. The experimentation team, knowing that anomalies threaten the experiment, must make every effort to detect and record them, correcting them when possible and excluding the impacted data or subjects when necessary.

Loss of Subjects

In spite of all the planning and preparation, situations arise that cause subjects to drop out of the experiment. There are ways to overcome this, but the development of a contingency plan is required. One way to overcome this is to schedule enough observers and trials that the loss of two or three subjects won't affect the statistical validity of the experiment. This will generally only work when the experiment deals with individual subjects. Another method is to train and have replacements ready to join the effort while in progress. This is more typical when experiment trials employ teams of subjects. A last resort is to have time built in for refresher training and use this time to train new subjects, but even this requires having a pool of subjects on standby. Sometimes, particularly if someone is lost well into the experiment after team dynamics are well-established, teams are simply asked to carry on short-handed. However, those teams will be working short-handed, which may impact their performance, so statistical tests of performance before and after the reduction in team size will be needed.

Loss of Observers/Controllers

Observers/controllers can also drop out of the experiment for various reasons. The ideal situation would be to have additional trained observers/ controllers in a standby position. These would likely be drawn from an organization located near the experiment venue, so that they could go about their daily routine while on standby. Failing that, a supervisor may be able to fill in, or observers can be transferred from less important stations to the more essential ones. This technique minimizes the impact of the loss. The importance of the data, the nature of the observation, and the resources available will dictate the nature of the contingency plan.

System Problems and Failures

The best way to mitigate against a system failure that destroys the experiment is to avoid single points of failure (one element that, if it fails, brings everything to a halt). This is generally achieved through redundancy. Failures can be avoided through a thorough, comprehensive test program that exercises all the elements prior to the experiment. A common problem that arises during testing is that the system is not as fully stressed during testing as it will be during the experiment. This leads to unexpected system crashes. The number of operational stations during the test period must equal the number of stations to be used during the experiment.

Data Contamination

Subjects in an experiment are often highly motivated to perform well. No matter how often they are told that they are not being evaluated, they still strive to excel. In some past experiments subjects have been able to learn about the scenario or get help from members of the experimentation team. In extreme cases, one or more of the subjects has deliberately sought to undermine the experiment. (There is an apocryphal story of a bored and frustrated young trooper in a field experiment deliberately inflicting friendly casualties.) As a consequence of any or all of these types of action, some parts of the data may be contaminated and lack the objectivity needed for analysis. If this occurs, the bad data will have to be excluded from the analysis.

Data Capture and Archiving

Data Preservation

In order for an experiment to contribute to knowledge generation, it must be replicable. This means, among other things, that the data must be preserved in their original form. The data should be copied before they are manipulated. Too many things can happen to alter the data once work begins. Data can lose its original format, be parsed, and be improperly categorized. In addition to archiving the data in their original form, a record must be kept of all the steps involved in manipulation of the data. This allows other analysts to reconstruct the analysis. For the sake of ensuring that data are saved, the prudent team saves them in more than one location and on more than one medium.

Privacy protection is also an important aspect. The data must be kept separate from the identities of the subjects. Care must be taken so that it is not possible to link the subjects with performance or data.

Data Reduction

Data reduction is an important function that frequently gets short-changed in practice. It is one thing to collect the data; it is another to convert them to a form that can be used by analysts. Generally, those most well-suited to perform data reduction are the data collectors. They are familiar with the data and their notations. Data reduction should occur as soon after the data collection as practical, preferably in the days immediately following the experiment. This has the benefit of performing the data reduction while experiment events are still fresh in the minds of the data collectors. It also has the added benefit of having all the collectors together so that they can work as a team. This is especially valuable when looking at data across nodes. Unfortunately, in some recent experiments data collectors were from a variety of organizations and on temporary duty for only the training and game days, with no time provided for data reduction. This practice invites difficulties and reflects a failure to develop a proper experimentation plan and/or allocate resources appropriately.

The participants in the data reduction process include all of the data collectors, data collection supervisors, and analysts. It is important that analysts participate because they will be able to guide the data collectors if they have a problem deciding how to code certain events, and they will better understand the data and its origins.

It is also important for the analysts to be present in the data reduction effort for cases where judgement is required in making coding decisions. Inter-coder reliability is vital. The analysts, because they see all the data, can spot where coders are differing in how they code the data and resolve these differences on the spot.

In many instances, the venue and systems used for the experiment is immediately used for other purposes. It is therefore imperative that data and other experiment artifacts (scenarios, event injections, survey forms, interview schedules, etc.) be archived immediately after the completion of the experiment to prevent it from being lost when the supporting systems are reconfigured for the next event.

In-Process and Quick Look Reporting

It has become common practice in training exercises to provide immediate feedback in the form of results while an exercise is still in process, as well as "quick look" reports all but immediately on completion of the formal exercise. While this makes perfect sense in a training environment, where prompt and authoritative feedback is one of the best ways to teach, it is not the proper approach to experimentation. It is imperative that this training tradition does not carry over to experimentation. Experimenters, sponsors of experiments, and decisionmakers need to realize that considerable analysis is often required to ascertain the results of an experiment. Instant feedback can (1) be misleading and (2) lead people to believe that they do not need to execute the data analysis plan.

Having said this, some data from experiments can be captured and presented quickly (in near real time). This is particularly true of data that evaluates systems – measuring load, throughput, frequency of use, etc. However, even this data is incomplete when first captured. The patterns in it must be read at the first order and in isolation from other information. Furthermore, this data is often not at the heart of the experimental hypothesis.

Having this system data quickly available is required so that it can be used to drive models and simulations in the post-experiment phase. Just because it is available does not mean one should share it. Sharing it without putting it into context (by complete analysis) can result in false and unwarranted conclusions being reached. Only when the analysis is completed can issues such as limits and interactive effects be studied.

It needs to be understood that much of the most valuable data collected cannot be extracted quickly. For example, the quality of shared awareness can only be assessed after what is known by individuals (not systems) is compared with ground truth. Similarly, shared awareness must wait until individual perceptions of the operating environment are compared with one another. Even simple system characteristics, such as the difference between information available in different command centers, cannot be examined until comparative analyses have occurred.

Strong reliance on immediate reporting and preliminary analysis also tends to drive out good findings and analysis. If decisionmakers' attention focuses on immediate results, those tend to stick – to become the primary learning from the experiment. Later results, particularly if they differ or show that alternative interpretations are more consistent with the data, have a tendency to be ignored. Cases have been reported where mid-level managers hesitated to put more considered analytic results forward because they were inconsistent with the initial reports.

The proper uses of in-progress and quick look reports are to spot trends and develop insights (hypotheses that might be checked later when better data and more time for analysis are available). If shared, they should not be briefed as conclusive or implying causality, and their preliminary nature should be emphasized. From the perspective of the experimentation team, the entire subject of experimentation products and scheduling is one in which both expectations and interpretations will need to be actively managed.

Example Experiment: Self-Synchronization

The illustrative self-synchronization experiment involved virtually every form of challenge an experimentation team can encounter. Their pretest was chaotic. They lost a trained observer at the last minute. The host institution failed to renew the license for their scenario driver, which came due between the pretest and the experiment. One of the subjects was called away on emergency leave. Moreover, their collaboration tool crashed during the second day of the experiment. However, because the experiment plan was robust and well-thought out, the experiment was still able to accomplish its objectives.

Here is how the events unfolded. First, the pretest training proved inadequate for both the observers and the subjects. Extra time had to be devoted to observing, classifying, and coding behaviors, particularly collaboration behaviors. The planned subject training in the use of collaboration tools and search tools failed to reach the level of proficiency specified for about 40 percent of the pretest subjects. Those with the greatest difficulty were found to be those with the least computer expertise and experience. Finally, subjects showed a clear tendency to impute today's characteristics to the sensors and communications systems available during the game.

The interval between the pretest and the experiment was busy. First, revised training was developed for observers and tested on a small new group, who were set up as a backup team for the experiment itself. Second, a qualification test for basic computer skills was developed to screen out subjects who would have difficulty mastering the systems they would need to employ during the experiment. In addition, the data analysis plan was adjusted to include statistical controls based on subject proficiency test results. Finally, the training for subjects was altered to stress the difference between the capabilities available during the game and those available today. These adjustments also caused the addition of one-half day to the training schedule.

As the start of the experiment approached, one of the experienced observers became ill. The existence of the standby observer team was, therefore validated as the best qualified replacement was moved into an active role. As the systems were being put into place for the experiment and tested, the scenario driver (commercial game) failed. A quick check found that the host institution had forgotten to renew the license for the system. An emergency purchase order was generated and the problem was promptly resolved.

The experiment started well. However, at the end of the first training day, one of the subjects was called home on emergency leave. She was replaced by her commander, who had to be given special training during off-duty hours to be ready for the start of the experiment runs. Data for her team was tagged to permit later analysis in order to determine whether her absence made a difference.

Finally, the collaboration tool, which was being used more heavily than expected and for functions not foreseen in the experiment plan, crashed on the second day of the experiment. Players were informed that a cyber-attack had taken out the system and play continued. Data from the period impacted were also tagged. The technical support team determined that more server capacity was needed. The system came back up after 6 hours and performed well from then on.

Among the lessons learned from our illustration experiments is the fact that things will not all go exactly as planned. Stuff happens. Subjects drop out immediately before and during experiments, observers get sick or are called away, systems fail, and scenarios bog down. Controllers need to be alert for problems. Solutions will often need to be conceived on the fly. Solutions and problems need to be thoroughly documented so that the analysis can take them into account.

---

[1]Given that transformational experiments are designed to test limits, it is difficult if not impossible to predict how subjects will use the systems.

CHAPTER 11

Products

G ood experimentation requires good documentation in order to provide a record of what went into its planning and what resulted from its execution. First and foremost, good documentation provides the basis for understanding experimentation results and judging their implications for transformation policy and investment decisions, without which they would have limited veracity and value to the DoD. Secondly, products that document and explain what went on before, during, and after an experiment carefully preserve a record of the scientific research accomplished. Finally, these products provide an archival basis for extending and integrating the experimentation results into the larger body of knowledge. This chapter takes a closer look at the various types of documentation required by experimentation, what information and knowledge they contain, and what purpose they are intended to serve. Additionally, we reflect upon a number of "best practice" principles that should be kept in mind when developing these various documentation products.

Types of Documentation Products and Their Use

Experiments are documented in a variety of ways, with each product serving the needs of a specific audience. Illustrated in Figure 11-1 are the principal products of interest in a typical experiment, although other types of reports, papers, briefings, or other products could be generated to meet the requirements of a specific experiment. As suggested from this figure, good documentation is required throughout the life cycle of the experiment, from pre-experiment planning to dissemination and archiving of results. Following this practice avoids a common misperception (carried over from exercise tradition) that the only documentation of significance is the so-called "quick look" briefing often provided to senior officials immediately following the completion of the event.

Management Plan

The management plan for the experiment, developed at the beginning of the pre-experimentation phase, provides the overall guidance for the experiment and specifies how the experiment will be planned and executed. In addition, this plan relates the experiment to the various external constituencies by articulating the various sponsor issues and stakeholder interests. Finally, the management plan provides the basis for securing support for the experiment from various participating military units, organizations, and other resources.

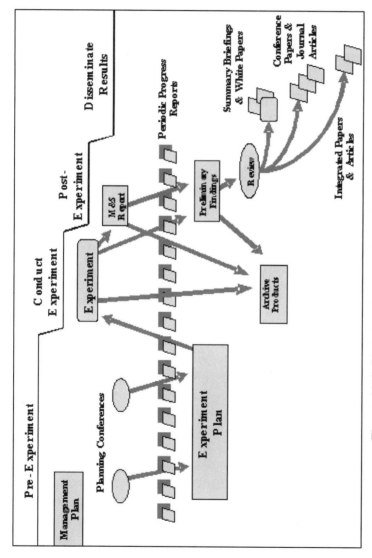

Figure 11-1. Management and Dissemination Products

Experiment Plan

A common mindset and practice of the past has been to treat the experiment plan as a loosely organized set of information papers or briefing slides that are circulated largely to inform senior officials about the purposes of the experiment, or to address specific aspects of the experiment (e.g., data collection plan). Very rarely are all of the various planning details brought together in a centrally maintained, integrated, and cohesive document. Such a sloppy and informal practice often leads to a fragmented understanding of how the experiment will come together to address critical questions, or how the various elements and participants will be synchronized. To avoid such problems, it is necessary to think of the experiment plan as being a living coordination document that communicates a consistent, comprehensive, and cohesive understanding of all of the planning details to every participant, supporter, and consumer of the experiment. An experiment plan is more than just a set of bulleted briefing slides. Like a military operations plan, it is the formal glue that holds the broad (and often diverse) experimentation community together and focuses them on a common set of objectives and intent.

Developed in accordance with the management plan, the experiment plan serves as the principal control vehicle for refining and documenting agreed details of the experiment. Maintained by the experiment manager, the experiment plan is a living document that is subject to revision and refinement throughout the course of the pre-experimentation phase. Documented within the experiment plan are the specific elements of the experiment outlined in Chapter 5, including a careful record of how each element is revised or refined during the pre-experiment phase. For example, these elements should address:

- Experimentation hypotheses and research questions;

- Experimentation treatments, baseline conditions, and controls;

- Experimentation subjects (including selection and training requirements);

- Experimentation scenarios;

- Definition of measures and data collection plan;

- Facility and other resource/asset requirements;

- Experimentation schedule (including pretest and rehearsal events); and

- Contingency options.

Because experimentation serves a broad set of constituencies, it is important that the experiment plan reflects multiple disciplines and perspectives, rather than being dominated by a single view. Proper scope and balance are crucial and reflect the critical, integrative role played by the experiment plan for achieving and maintaining synchronization among the various participants. Good experiments and productive learning do not just happen by accident or wishful thinking. Rather, they are the products of various professional communities coming together via conscious and comprehensive planning that is articulated and coordinated via a good Experiment Plan. To quote the South African professional golfer, Gary Player, "The harder you work, the luckier you get." A good experiment plan effectively communicates the product of this hard work.

Planning Conferences

To achieve this level of articulation and coordination, it is often necessary to hold one or more planning conferences for a specific experiment. Planning conferences represent a major element in the planning of large and comprehensive experiments. However, they also constitute part of the documentation process since their deliberations and findings ultimately feed back into the experiment plan. They become necessary because of the sheer complexity of negotiating and coordinating the myriad of details involved in a successful experiment. Planning conferences bring together the key participants, peer reviewers, and supporting organizations at critical junctures in the planning process in order to (1) focus attention on major "show stoppers," (2) identify the strategy and means for overcoming each obstacle to conducting the experiment, and (3) document the inter-organizational agreements and commitments that produce a successful experiment. The timing and frequency of planning conferences depend upon the specific scope and complexity of the experiment. Planning conferences can be convened to address major, emerging issues, or be set on a prescribed schedule (e.g., Joint Forces Command experiments typically include an initial planning conference, a mid-term planning conference, and a final product conference).

Periodic Progress Reports

Periodic progress reports, typically issued by the experiment manager on a regular basis to the sponsors, stakeholders, supporting organizations, and key participants, serve as a vehicle that focuses attention on coordination and synchronization issues between major planning conferences. Like these conferences, progress reports provide a vehicle for obtaining and documenting organizational commitment and support for the experimentation, although the issues addressed might be of a lesser scope and significance. Responses to each progress report are circulated for coordination and then reflected as revisions to the experiment plan. In this manner, progress reports can remain focused on coordination and synchronization issues, while the living experiment plan continues to serve as the principal archive of agreements and commitments.

As shown in Figure 11-1, it is important that progress reports are issued throughout the entire life cycle of an experiment. A past weakness of some military experiments has been the tendency of participating organizations to quickly lose interest once an experiment has been executed, thus making it difficult to maintain access to key personnel who can make valuable contributions during the post-experiment analysis and documentation phases. In response, the experiment manager should consider using the progress reports as a vehicle for maintaining the necessary access and commitment needed to properly complete the experimentation life cycle.

Modeling and Simulation Report (When Appropriate)

As discussed in Chapter 5, many good experiments will seek to explore and extend the empirical findings through an adjunct modeling and simulation effort. This work, often undertaken during the analysis phase of the experiment, can serve to examine a broader range of conditions and variables than could be feasibly addressed in the actual experiment. Since these results form an equally important part of the analysis, they require proper integration and documentation with other aspects of the experimentation. Depending upon the level of modeling and simulation work undertaken, the results can either be documented in a separate report (as shown in Figure 11-1) or directly incorporated into the report of the main analysis of the experiment. When such modeling and simulation are performed as a major study by a separate organization, it is appropriate that a separate report be developed in order for the additional assumptions and other analytical considerations to be uniquely recognized and fully documented. At the end of the day, however, the modeling and simulation results need to be folded back into the main experimentation analysis.

Preliminary Findings Report

A frequently noted weakness of many past military experiments is the tendency to maintain the findings and interpretations in a "close hold" manner until the publication of a final "approved" report. Such a practice reflects a lack of appreciation for the true nature of experimentation (i.e., what constitutes success or failure) and a fear that the experiment might cast specific programs or other initiatives in a negative light. However, this practice represents a disservice to the scientific validity and operational relevance of the experimentation. Good experimentation always (subject to security restrictions) allows for proper review and critique of the findings by both (1) participating subjects, observers, controllers, analysts, and support team members and (2) external sponsors, stakeholders, and peer reviewers. This review serves two related purposes. First, the review provides an opportunity for the empirical findings to be rigorously reviewed and interpreted by multiple disciplines and perspectives. The synthesis of these multiple perspectives is crucial for developing a deep understanding of the issues and complexity surrounding the development of mission capability packages. Second, this review strengthens and validates the analytic "audit trail" that relates the limited context of the experimentation to the broader questions associated with transformation policy and investment decisions.

As noted in the following section of this chapter, the content and format of the final report needs to be tailored to the specific needs and interests of the different audiences served by the experiment (e.g., senior defense officials, members of the defense research and development community, and military historians and futurists). Accordingly, the preliminary findings report should address these broad sets of interests and allow the various constituencies to gain an initial understanding of what the experiment produced. In doing so, however, it is important that care is taken in distinguishing findings from interpretations.

Reporting Findings

Findings are simply the reported outcomes of the experiment, usually a combination of quantitative or statistical comparisons of the various cases or treatments examined in the experiment, supplemented or amplified by qualitative observations and assessments gleaned from subject matter expert observers. In addition, findings generally include (or specifically reference) the basic observations and data collected in the experiment along with the important artifacts (scenarios, constraints, probes, training, etc.) associated with the experiment. Findings are reported in a concise and carefully documented manner since they are intended to convey an objective impression of what transpired in the experiment, and provide a basis for the various constituencies to contextually judge the outcome of the experiment.

Likewise, findings typically serve to focus attention on important or significant outcome differences found among the cases or treatments addressed in the experiment. In some cases, depending upon the nature of the questions or hypotheses being addressed, it is also important to highlight situations in which no differences were found. Focusing on outcome differences (or the lack of differences) gets to the heart of why experiments are conducted in the first place. To merely say that a new doctrinal concept, new piece of technology, or new organizational structure produced a good warfighting outcome is not sufficient since it holds little meaning for any audience. Rather, the key findings of the experiment should center on how this outcome compared to that of a baseline case or some other meaningful conditions. Failure to emphasize comparative findings has often been the most frequently observed weakness of past military experiments.

Reporting Interpretations

By contrast, interpretations reflect the application of experienced judgment to the experiment findings. Interpretations are subjective in nature and involve drawing inferences and/or implications from the objectively reported findings. Hence, care should be taken to distinguish findings from interpretations in the reporting of an experiment. Like findings, interpretations occupy an important (but different) place in the reports of the experiment since they allow the various constituencies the opportunity to view the outcome of the experiment from different points of view. Thus, interpretations serve a legitimate role in the experiment reports, provided that they are clearly distinguished from objective findings and that they are properly attributed to a particular point of view.

Dissemination of the Preliminary Findings Report

The preliminary findings report should be circulated for comment by appropriate audiences, usually within a reasonably short period of time after the initial analysis phase (including the modeling and simulation work) has been completed. At the same time, the experiment manager must ensure that this review is completed in an orderly and timely manner (perhaps a few weeks) and that it does not extend into an unending debate among different perspectives and interests. To accomplish this, the experiment manager needs to have the strong support of sponsors and stakeholders, who have agreed beforehand on a set of review and publication schedules.

Final Products for External Audiences

Since transformation experiments are of interest to a broad audience, it is only natural that their findings and interpretations be documented in a variety of tailored products. One such product includes summary briefings and white papers that focus on the implications of experimentation findings for transformation policy and investment decisions. Typically, these briefings and papers are aimed at senior defense officials and are geared to highlight the operational aspects of the experimentation and to interpret/summarize the findings in the terms of military capability improvements, operational concepts, and associated operational risks. At the same time, these documents illustrate the interdependent nature of the elements making up a mission capability package. Finally, these documents tend to be written in a concise manner that immediately draws attention to the major insights and conclusions drawn from the experiment.

In contrast to this set of "executive level" products, a set of products needs to be developed for the research and development community. These include technical conference papers and refereed journal articles that are aimed more at the research and development community. Here, these papers will typically focus on specific theoretical or propositional issues of interest to specific professional forums such as the Institute of Electrical and Electronics Engineers (IEEE), the American Institute of Aeronautics and Astronautics (AIAA), the American Psychological Society (APS), the Human Factors Society (HFS), and the Military Operations Research Society (MORS). The venue for presenting such papers includes any number of workshops, symposia, conferences, and professional journals sponsored by these organizations. As opposed to the summary nature of the executive level papers and briefings aimed at senior defense officials, these more academic products will often describe selected aspects of the experimentation in extensive academic detail. Additionally, these technical products will often focus greater emphasis on placing and interpreting the detailed findings of the experiment within the context of the existing research literature. Finally, these products will focus more on how the available empirical evidence has led to the support and refinement of specific bodies of theory (e.g., network centric operations, sensemaking, collaboration).

Finally, a third set of products includes integrated papers and articles that place the set of experiment findings in an overall defense transformation framework. Such products tend to combine an operational and force development focus with a rigorous analytic presentation in order to examine the broader implications of the experimentation for the professional military audience. Here, a likely venue of publication will include senior service school journals, military trade and association magazines, the annual Command and Control Research and Technology Symposium (CCRTS), the biannual International Command and Control Research and Technology Symposium (ICCRTS), NATO or coalition working groups, and other national and international military forums that can expose these results to a broad military audience. Accordingly, the integrated papers and articles should appeal to a broad readership and be organized along the major themes of defense transformation.

Archiving the Experiment for Future Investigations

Experiments seldom have more than limited relevance or utility in isolation, hence their findings and interpretations should usually be placed in a broader context. In Chapter 4, the concept of the experimentation campaign was introduced along with a discussion of how knowledge and understanding are often developed through a cumulative series of individual experiments. However, it would be a mistake to interpret an experimentation campaign as only being a set of individual experiments strung together. Rather, an experimentation campaign can be characterized as a well-designed sequence of investigations that successively builds knowledge within an organized framework of questions, hypotheses, performance and outcome measures, and associated empirical evidence. Even if a specific experiment has not been anticipated to form part of a larger campaign, it is often instructive and useful to compare and integrate future findings with those obtained in a previous experiment. Given this broader context, consideration must be given to preserving the methodology and original empirical evidence in a form that makes it available to future studies and experimentation.

The requirement to carefully archive each experiment is different from the management and dissemination purposes discussed earlier in this chapter. In one sense, archival documentation is aimed more toward an internal, practitioner audience within the operations research, analysis, and experimentation communities rather than at an external, consumer audience. Secondly, the body of empirical evidence from each experiment is archived so that it can be made available to others for subsequent analysis and integration with other experimentation efforts. Finally, the archival documentation contributes to the refinement of experimentation methodology, measurement and assessment instruments, and modeling and simulation techniques - all interests of an internal, practitioner community.

As shown in Figure 11-2, a variety of archiving products should be developed from both the planning and execution of the experiment. Each type of product reflects a specific content and serves a specific purpose.

Original Data Records, Transcripts, and Other Artifacts

Data records, interview transcripts, and other artifacts of the experiment (e.g., scenario materials, injections/probes, background books, training materials) should be collected immediately after execution of the experiment and preserved in their original form. This can include a variety of both electronic and hand-written materials such as audio/video tape recordings, telemetry files, computer modeling output, voice and digital message traffic, SME observer and assessment forms, interview notes, and survey forms. In some cases, preservation of this material might be based upon legal requirements (e.g., Use of Human Subject requirements); however, the main purpose of preserving the original material is to make it available to future studies for refined analysis and synthesis. Experience with past experimentation has demonstrated that, with the passage of time, new questions will arise or new perspectives will be developed that can shed new light on existing

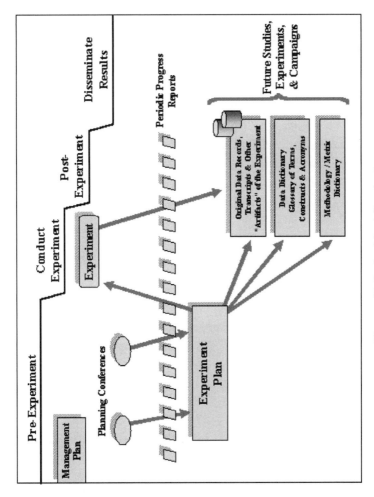

Figure 11-2. Archival Products

data. Making these data available to future studies and experimentation offers the opportunity for refining the interpretation of data or making comparative assessments, a hallmark of scientific experimentation.

In preserving original records, transcripts, and other artifacts, consideration should be given to selecting an appropriate repository organization. This organization should provide a mechanism for both (1) promoting awareness of the material across the DoD research community and (2) providing appropriate access to the material. The length of time for maintaining the material will depend upon the nature and significance of the experiment, possibly lasting years, or even decades as in the case of "classic" or "seminal" experiments.

Data Dictionary/Glossary of Terms, Constructs, and Acronyms

Perhaps the most frustrating aspect of comparing research findings across different experiments is the frequent lack of consistency regarding the definition of key terms, constructs, and acronyms. This is particularly true when one moves beyond the engineering terminology associated with the physical domain and into the more subjective terminology associated with the information and cognitive domains. Without consistency of meaning, the comparison and integration of findings across experiments becomes problematic at best. Thus, a fundamental requirement for experimentation campaigns (and a good principle to follow in general) is proper documentation of the terms, constructs, and acronyms to be used in the experiments. Specifically, for the information and cognitive domains, the documentation should include accepted operational definitions of each term/construct/measure, accompanied by whatever contextual information is required to ensure consistent interpretation in future research.

As noted earlier, the consumer of data dictionaries and glossaries is primarily the internal, practitioner audience within the DoD and international research and development communities. Thus, dissemination of this information can be both internal to the Services or Joint commands, and via the CCRP website, MORS, and various NATO or coalition working groups. Ultimately, much of this material can be incorporated into future Codes of Best Practice or propositional inventories maintained by the practitioner community.

Methodology / Metric Dictionary

Considerable time, effort, and creativity often go into the development of measurement and assessment instruments that can accurately illuminate the structures, processes, and functioning of a military operation. As with key terms and constructs, however, it is important to achieve consistency across different experiments. Thus, an important product of any experiment is the proper documentation of how these various instruments were developed and employed. This consistency provides the basis for both (1) comparing empirical evidence across different experiments within a campaign and (2) extending and refining the measurement and assessment instruments within the practitioner community. While this task is relatively straightforward for engineering methodologies applied to the physical domain, greater challenges exist within the information and cognitive domains. Within these domains, it is important to document the accepted dimensional definitions and metric scales employed as part of each instrument, accompanied by whatever contextual information is required to ensure consistent interpretation and use in future research.

As with key terms and constructs, the consumer of measurement/metric dictionaries is primarily the internal, practitioner audience within the DoD and international research and development communities. Thus, the dissemination of this information can be both internal to the Services or Joint commands, and via the CCRTS and ICCRTS conferences, MORS workshops and symposiums, and various NATO or coalition working groups. Ultimately, much of this material can be incorporated into future Codes of Best Practice maintained by the practitioner community.

Key Considerations: Products and Their Dissemination

Experimentation provides essential support for informing and supporting defense transformation. For this to occur, however, it is important that the experimentation products that are disseminated for each of the different audiences give proper consideration to several issues:

- What are the different questions being addressed at each stage in the transformation process?

- What are the relevant perspectives of the multiple sponsors and stakeholders?

- What types of evidence should be considered and how should this evidence be forged into a cohesive story that supports transformation policy and investment decisions?

- What type of audience is being informed by a particular dissemination product?

Product Focus Depends Upon the Type of Experiment

As noted in Chapter 1, experiments of various kinds have begun to proliferate throughout the DoD as part of the general interest in defense transformation. In Chapter 2, these experiments were further broken down into three categories or uses: discovery experiments, hypothesis testing experiments, and demonstration experiments. Accordingly, what is documented will depend, in some degree, upon the purpose of the experiment and the level of maturity reflected in the experiment. Discovery experiments focus on novel systems, concepts, organizational structures, technologies, and other elements in a setting where they can be explored, observed, and cataloged. Quite often, a major emphasis in their documentation will be the important constructs and relationships discovered during the experiment. Here, it is important that the products identify the potential military benefits suggested by the experiment, to document emerging concepts of employment, and to begin articulating hypotheses for future experimentation. At this stage of experimentation, decisionmakers rely upon experimentation products to weed out ideas that will not work, refine the ideas that seem promising, and lay out a framework for further research and development. While results at this stage of experimentation are often tentative, documentation can support future research and development investment decisions by addressing the following questions:

- What new performance variables or relationships have been introduced or strongly affected by the systems, concepts, processes, and structures?

- What new constructs have emerged that require more careful observation and measurement in future experiments?

- What are the important contextual features and boundary conditions that enable or prevent the systems, concepts, processes, and structures from making an operational contribution?

By contrast, hypothesis testing experiments reflect a more classic approach to experimentation, which seeks to examine carefully constructed comparisons among alternative cases (including a baseline case) under carefully constructed conditions in order to provide supportive evidence for carefully articulated propositions. Thus, a major emphasis in their products is the rigorous documentation of experiment assumptions and controls, the empirical data and their analysis, and the level of evidence supporting each hypothesis. At this stage of experimentation, decisionmakers look to the experimentation products to validate specific transformation initiatives by addressing the following questions:

- Do the comparative findings make a military difference (operational significance)?

- Are the comparative findings reliable, given the experimentation sample size (statistical significance)?

- To what extent can the findings be generalized to real-world military operational conditions (experimental controls)?

Finally, demonstration experiments offer an opportunity to demonstrate the efficacy of a new system, concept, process, or structure under carefully orchestrated conditions. Additionally, demonstration experiments often afford the opportunity to examine the combined effect of two or more such initiatives, thus balancing decisionmaker attention across several elements that comprise a mission capability package. In contrast to the first two types of experiments, demonstration experiments are not about documenting new knowledge. Rather, the purpose of the documentation is to communicate the demonstrated capability to those decisionmakers unfamiliar with it. Good documentation can support critical transformation investment and fielding decisions by refining the answers to the following questions:

- What is the critical range of conditions over which the demonstrated capability can be expected to exist?

- What is the complete set of initiatives that must be pursued in order to produce a robust mission capability package?

Reporting Implications for Mission Capability Packages

It is clear from Chapter 2 that the objectives of experimentation are to develop and refine innovative concepts of operation in the form of mission capability packages. To accomplish this objective, experimentation must consider a broad range of perspectives that includes (but is not limited to) the various DOTMLPF elements. A weakness of many past military experiments has been a preoccupation with technology at the expense of adequately documenting other aspects of the operation. If experimentation is to truly support the development of mission capability packages, then it is important that the documentation captures multiple perspectives on what is being addressed and discovered, rather than narrowly focusing only on materiel technology issues. Beyond the more familiar (and more easily measured) aspects of technology performance, such perspectives can include:

- Doctrinal lessons learned (e.g., the validation of new theories of warfare or new principles of operation);

- Personnel performance and training effectiveness (e.g., the adaptability of leaders and soldiers/airmen/seamen to new technologies, tactics, and procedures); and

- Organizational dynamics and performance (e.g., the ability of new organizational structures to support new forms of leadership and collaboration).

The broad nature of the issues involved in defense transformation requires the use of a multidisciplinary team for developing the experimentation products. Such a team not only reflects expertise from each of the DOTMLPF communities, but is also (as a whole) sensitive to the various challenges associated with building integrated mission capability packages. Expertise from each community is required in order to articulate each perspective in an appropriate and insightful manner. Overall perspective is required in order to balance the presentation of the issues in the various experimentation products.

Document All of the Evidence

While it is true that all experimentation, by definition, produces empirical evidence, it is not true that all empirical evidence comes in the singular form of precise engineering metrics (e.g., geographic coverage, bandwidth, kills/engagement). Just as good documentation considers multiple perspectives on an experiment, so too will that same documentation seek to organize and synthesize multiple classes of evidence. Here, the three classes of evidence are:

- Quantified, objective measures of engineering performance;

- Calibrated, observable measures of behavioral and organizational performance; and

- Subject matter expert judgment of outcome.

Each of these classes of evidence corresponds to different types of capability and performance issues being addressed in the experiment. Each class of evidence provides a critical ingredient in the final story being written about the experiment.

Quantified, objective measures of engineering performance are considered the "gold standard" of scientific experimentation because they allow outcomes and findings to be documented in a defined, reliable, and replicable manner. Without such a documentation standard, a comparison of findings from one treatment or case to another becomes problematic, thus negating much of the value and purpose of experimentation in the defense transformation process.

In the case of behavioral and organizational performance, however, much of what transpires in an experiment cannot be directly observed or measured in an engineering sense. Hence, other approaches must be taken to documenting this aspect of an experiment. Unfortunately, too often in the past, such dimensions and variables have been routinely ignored because they were considered too hard to document. By contrast, however, the social sciences provide a variety of well-accepted methods for observing and documenting behavioral and organizational performance in a structured manner. In most cases, it is simply a matter of expending the time and resources necessary to properly understand and apply these methods. However, this investment in time and energy will yield appropriate dividends. Capturing this type of evidence in an experiment is critical because much of the success in exploiting new military technologies will be dependent upon how human operators and decisionmakers react and interact (both individually and collectively) with these technologies. Ignoring this class of evidence results in telling only half of the story of the experiment.

The third class of evidence, subject matter expert opinion, is valuable because of the experienced insights that it typically brings to an experiment. However, the documentation of such evidence must recognize the scientific limitations and biases of such evidence. Subject matter experts, despite their experience, suffer from the same judgmental biases as other human beings, hence their contributions cannot be substituted for sound statistical analysis of more objective, structured, and quantified measures. Here, over-reliance on this class of evidence in documenting the findings of an experiment can be problematic.

There have been several weaknesses that have been often observed in past military experiments.

There has been a tendency to document only what can be easily measured and quantified (i.e., focus experimentation reports and other products only on measures of engineering performance). Without placing this information in the context of other classes of empirical evidence, these results are misleading, they can miss the "big picture," and they are often irrelevant to the questions posed by senior decisionmakers. In cases that go beyond technical data, there has been a tendency to collect and document only SME opinion, usually in the form of summary judgments by senior "gray beards" selected because of their interest in a particular transformation initiative. While this approach attempts to focus on the "big picture" findings of an experiment, it suffers from a lack of scientific rigor and precision insight. Documentation that reflects only SME judgment not only runs the risk of being self-serving and biased, but also discredits the entire notion of scientific experimentation.

By contrast, good experimentation (as anticipated and documented in the experiment plan) seeks to exploit the strengths of each of these three classes of evidence and to present a balanced picture of this evidence to decisionmakers. Recognizing that different aspects of the experiment are best captured by different classes of empirical evidence, the experimentation team must work to integrate and document multiple threads of analysis into a cohesive story, a story that relates the various findings and insights of the experimentation to potential transformation investment decisions. As noted earlier, this challenge will require a multi-disciplinary team that can perform several critical functions:

- Select and combine the appropriate classes of evidence for illuminating and supporting each major insight or finding;

- Seek, where possible, to cross-validate one class of evidence with other classes of evidence addressing the same experimentation issue;

- Compare these insights and findings with both operational experience and the broader body of research literature;

- Communicate across functional or DOTMLPF community boundaries to relate the different insights and findings within the context of an integrated mission capability package; and

- Weave the various insights and findings into supportable arguments that address specific transformation investment decisions.

Tailoring Products to Various Audiences

Dissemination products serve different audiences, hence they must be individually tailored to the interests of these audiences. As noted earlier in this chapter, these audiences include:

- Senior defense officials concerned with immediate transformation policy and investment decisions and their associated risks and opportunities;

- Members of the defense research and development community concerned with the theoretical and technical issues being explored in a given experiment; and

- Military historians, futurists, and conceptual thinkers concerned with placing the experimentation results in a broader context of defense transformation.

Given the different needs and interests of these three different audiences, it is unlikely that a single report, paper, or briefing would serve to effectively communicate the findings and interpretations of a given experiment. Accordingly, the dissemination products aimed at each type of audience must be consciously focused and written in a manner that is best understood by each recipient.

Decision papers, summary reports, and briefings aimed at senior defense officials must be written in a manner and tone that relates experiment details to real-world, operational issues and considerations. These dissemination products focus attention on the key implications for transformation policy and investment decisions. As part of this focus, products must carefully distinguish findings from interpretations and address the operational "So what?" questions, rather than merely reciting experiment outcomes. Additionally, they should carefully outline the limitations of the experiment so that decisionmakers understand the key risks and uncertainties still surrounding a particular policy or investment issue. In this manner, the products serve to justify the investment in the experiment and help to articulate the role and utility of experimentation in the defense transformation process.

By contrast, scientific papers, reports, and briefings aimed at members of the defense research and development community are written with a more technical tone and often with a specific technical focus. These dissemination products will focus attention on the key theoretical, technical, and propositional issues addressed in the experiment. As part of this focus, these products place experiment outcomes in the context of existing technical knowledge by addressing and emphasizing the scientific and engineering "Why?" questions. Additionally, they serve to highlight the relationships that exist among key materiel, behavioral, process, and organizational variables. Their purpose is to inform research and development personnel in a scientifically rigorous manner so that the experimentation results can contribute to a larger body of scientific and engineering knowledge. In this manner, the products serve to establish the scientific credibility of experimentation in the defense transformation process.

Finally, white papers, articles, and books aimed at a broad audience of military historians, futurists, and conceptual thinkers tend to reflect an integrated perspective on both operational and technical issues. These dissemination products place the experiment outcomes in the context of broad transformational themes (e.g., Network Centric

Warfare, Information Age warfare, effects-based operations, and asymmetric warfare). Here, the focus might be placed on interpreting the experiment outcomes in the light of historical military case studies, projecting their implications for future operational scenarios, or integrating these findings with other studies and experiments to develop broader doctrinal and force structure conclusions. The critical question often addressed in this type of paper or article is "Where do we go from here?" As such, these dissemination products are often used to stimulate new conceptual thinking and to motivate the undertaking of new areas of research. In this manner, the products serve to guide and extend the transformation process within the DoD.

Tying it all Together: Documenting Experimentation Campaigns

As noted earlier in Chapter 4, experimentation campaigns represent a systematic approach to successively refining knowledge and understanding in a specific transformation area. The value of an experimentation campaign exceeds that of a collection of individual experiments precisely because of the integrated and cohesive learning that takes place over an orchestrated set of experiments. But for this broader learning to take place, the synthesis of findings and interpretations from across several related experiments must be accomplished in a scientific or professional manner.

The synthesis of findings and interpretations from any set of studies or experiments is always enabled through careful documentation. In the case of experimentation campaigns, the documentation serves to weave the individual findings and interpretations into a cohesive story that addresses one or more transformation themes. As in the case of a single experiment, the products of an experimentation campaign should be tailored to specific audiences: senior defense officials; members of the defense research and development community; and those with a broader historical, futurist, or conceptual focus. Thus, the focus and tone of each product should be carefully matched to the interests and needs of the intended audience.

Regardless of the audience, however, the principal challenge in the documentation of experimentation campaigns is to present the set of findings and interpretations in a consistent and purposeful manner. This places an additional burden on both the managers of individual experiments and those responsible for the broader experimentation campaigns. Such a challenge underscores the need to carefully document each individual experiment since the authors of the campaign papers, reports, and other products will draw heavily on these previous documents for their· raw material. If critical assumptions, conditions, and limitations have not been accurately captured in these previous documents, then the likelihood for some misinterpretation and inappropriate conclusions remains high. By contrast, the development of campaign dissemination products should follow accepted scientific practices of carefully citing the specific document references of each finding or interpretation. Only by careful documentation and thorough and complete citation is it possible to translate the long-term investment in an experimentation campaign into useful guidance for defense transformation.

Conclusion

Good documentation of experiments goes well beyond the creation of a few action officer briefing slides, a set of press releases, or a "quick look" briefing, an approach taken all too often in the past. Experiments need to be carefully documented throughout their life cycle by means of a specific set of management, dissemination, and archival products. The specific focus and tone of these products must be matched to their particular audiences. This reflects both good practice and common sense since each type of audience will be looking at the experiment to provide answers to a different set of questions. In addition, these products will also be shaped by the degree of maturity reflected in an experiment (i.e., discovery, hypothesis testing, and demonstration) since, again, different questions are posed at each stage.

Likewise, the documentation of experiments must reflect a broad set of perspectives, rather than being held captive by a particular set of technology interests. This is true for two related reasons. First, the successful planning and execution of a good experiment requires the support and synchronized participation of a diverse set of DOTMLPF communities. Secondly, the experiment should serve to shed light on a broad set of transformation issues typically associated with developing mission capability packages.

Finally, there is a degree of both science and art reflected in the good documentation of experiments. First, experiments should be documented in a scientific manner, following the accepted practices of the engineering and research professions. Careful, professional documentation preserves an objective record of what the experiment produced and provides a solid foundation for drawing a range of operational, scientific, and investment/policy inferences from the empirical evidence obtained in the experiment. At the same time, good documentation reflects the art of skillful communication. Since the purpose of experimentation is discovery and learning, this evidence must be assembled and communicated in a way that highlights the comparative findings and differences revealed by the experiment. Only in this manner does the experiment contribute in a meaningful way to the support of transformation investment and policy decisions, the maturation of technology, and the refinement of warfighting theory. Both science and art are essential ingredients to good documentation and must be properly considered for the DoD to obtain appropriate return on investment in the experiment.

CHAPTER 12

Model-Based Experiments

Overview

M odels and simulations have a role, albeit a different one, in support of all three uses of experiments: discovery, hypothesis testing, and demonstration. As a well-crafted experimentation campaign matures, the roles and characteristics of the models and simulations in use coevolve with changes in the operational concepts and technologies.

This chapter describes a special kind of experimentation, a model-based experiment, in which models, most likely in the form of simulations (executable models), substitute for human subjects and military hardware in the experimentation process and are the sources of the data. The same principles, articulated in Chapters 4 and 5, apply to model-based experiments just as they apply to empirically-based experimentation. Model-based experiments still require extensive pre-experiment effort, must be supported by a multidisciplinary team, and must adhere to the scientific method.

There are many situations in which model-based experimentation is the preferred method for generating experimentation "data." In fact, there are times when they are the only mechanism for achieving the desired insights. Given that the transformation of the DoD focuses on the future, a time for which empirical data is hard to find, model-based experimentation can be expected to be useful in exploring the possibilities. The DoD's strategy for transformation involves the coevolution of mission capability packages. The MCP concept recognizes the need for systematic and simultaneous change in how the military functions along multiple dimensions-change needed to leverage Information Age technologies. At an overview level, three types of things are changing:

- *People* - this includes the numbers, skills, and ways in which they are organized for operations;

- *Process* - how members of the military organization, coalition, or interagency team accomplish their responsibilities; and

- *Infrastructure* - the systems, federations of systems, technologies, and other material resources that are applied in support of military operations.

Models can represent elements of a system and explore how they interact. This can be helpful in searching for two kinds of insights. First, there may be insights about the binding constraints on the performance of the system(s) or federation of systems. For example, one might observe that increasing communications bandwidth between HQ's A and B did not improve B's situation awareness. A simulation might demonstrate that the binding constraint on B's performance is a limited ability to process (fuse) the data that they are already receiving. Therefore, additional communications capacity could in fact prove to be of limited value.

Second, there may be insights related to uncertainties that could affect force performance. For example, consider a situation where a significant number of chemical attacks are perceived by troops in an area of operations. The reporting associated with these types of events place large demands on the command and control systems. These demands might inhibit other types of communications and information related to other aspects of the situation. This interference with other information flows could have unanticipated consequences on operations (e.g., ATO processes, maneuver control). A simulation experiment would be a very efficient way of exploring the robustness of a command and control system when subjected to extreme circumstances, and for exploring command and control logic that might increase the robustness of a given command and control system under extreme conditions.

Model-based experimentation has its most obvious utility in support of discovery and hypothesis testing experiments. Some specific reasons for choosing a model-based experiment include:

- Efficiently (both in terms of cost and time) exploring a set of scenarios, operational concepts, and technologies for combinations of circumstances that appear to be fruitful opportunities for further exploration using human subjects and hardware (discovery);

• Supplementing other experiments with simulation experiments that evaluate the concepts and technologies under a broader set of conditions. This data can then help to more completely inform additional experimentation, acquisition, doctrine, and force structure decisions (discovery and hypothesis testing);

• Extension, or evaluating the results of a tested concept in a different context. An example would be to use the data from a JTF HQ command and control experiment as input to a constructive combat simulation that assesses the operational contribution of the HQ's performance improvement, or placing limited experiment results into an entire mission capability package and simulating overall force performance (discovery and hypothesis testing);

• Decomposing an entire MCP that was tested in a live experiment, and exploring changes in specific components (discovery and hypothesis testing);

• Exploring the potential utility of technologies that may not yet exist. An example being the use of small agile robots as an integral part of urban combat operations (discovery);

- Efficiently evaluating the suitability of proposed metrics (dependent variables) that are being considered for application in an experiment or experimentation campaign (discovery and hypothesis testing); and

- Inexpensively replicating a concept and set of technologies that were demonstrated in and ACTD for explanatory purposes (demonstration).

There are two major benefits to be gained from properly crafted model-based experimentation. First, the rules of logic that apply to modeling and quantification bring discipline to thinking that is often necessary to address complex problems effectively. A related benefit of good modeling is that it reduces a situation of interest to its essential elements, focusing the experimentation team on the important issues. Second, insight into very complex issues and systems requires iteration between analysis and synthesis. Scientists, analysts, subject matter experts, and decisionmakers must be able to understand how a system decomposes into its component parts, and how it behaves in its totality. Good modeling supports both of these requirements efficiently.

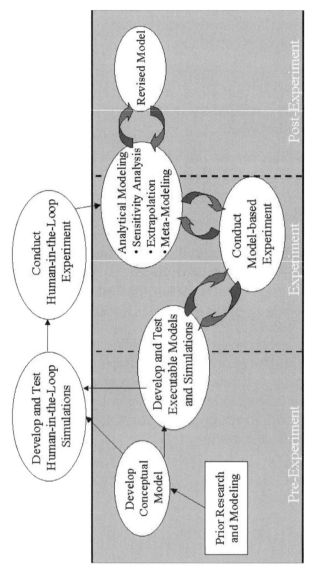

Figure 12-1. Modeling and Simulation in Experimentation

The Anatomy of a Model-Based Experiment

The principles that should be considered for successfully conducting a model-based experiment are the same as those identified in Chapter 5. Figure 12-1 highlights the subset of the modeling discussed in Chapter 5 with which we are concerned.

There are differences in specific requirements for model-based experimentation that in some ways make model-based experiments easier. But there are also differences that make them much more challenging. Perhaps the biggest pitfall in model-based experimentation is the failure to recognize the importance of the subtleties in modeling. This section attempts to highlight some of the subtleties that should be considered. The sequencing of this discussion maps to the stages of the experimentation process identified earlier.

Pre-Experiment Phase

The basic principles in Chapter 5, highlighting the need for detailed preparation, also apply to model-based experimentation. A point to emphasize for model-based experiments is that the essential activity in the pre-experiment phase is to identify the goals of the experiment. Depending on the type of experiment, these goals could be stated as a priori hypotheses (hypothesis testing experiment), or as desired improvements in Information Age command and control, like a continuously adaptive Air Tasking Order (discovery experiment). The expression of these goals provides the foundation for all subsequent activities. They support the selection of relevant measures and metrics, help to identify the necessary skills in the team, and will help to bound the types of existing models and tools that are applicable to the experiment.

Developing, tailoring, and employing models and simulations should be done by multidisciplinary teams. The team should consist of experts as well as stakeholders in the experiment (Figure 12-2). This often requires special attention in model-based experiments because many of the issues that might cause a concept to fail in a full experiment will only become evident in a model-based experiment if they are represented in the model. An example might be communications representation. In an experiment, if there is no connectivity, then the players in the experiment are unable to share information, and the need for communications and a communications expert are obvious. On the model side, many simulations embed assumptions regarding communications capacity, or information dissemination delays (and concepts). Obtaining reasonable behavior of a model along this dimension will require coordination between communications specialists (or technologists for advanced concepts) and modelers. Otherwise, a model may have embedded (implicit) assumptions or gaps in logic that are essential considerations for evaluating the experimental tool or concept.

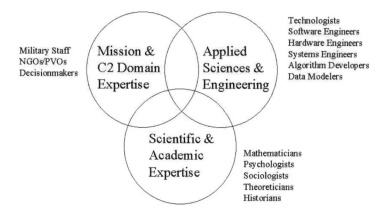

Figure 12-2. Multidisciplinary Modeling Team

There are some analogies that can be drawn between modeling terminology and experimentation terminology that can help clarify our thinking in relation to formulation of an experiment. Specifically:

- *Independent variables* in experiments are equivalent to the subset of the model's input data. Those that we choose to vary are called *controllable variables*. Those that will not be varied are called *uncontrollable variables*. In effect, the controllable variables equal the treatments in an experiment.

- *Dependent variables* (experimentation data) in experiments are equivalent to the output data or target variables in models. In both cases, these should be clearly defined metrics that are selected for their relevance to the goals of the experiment. The NATO *Code of Best Practices for C2 Assessment*[1] provides an excellent supporting discussion on metrics.

- *Intervening variables* in experiments are equivalent to the remaining data, algorithms, and logic in a model that either provides context for the model, or describe some relevant cause-and-effect relationship among independent and dependent variables.

Identifying what we already know is an essential part of the pre-experiment phase. The principles concerning the identification of relevant operational knowledge, organizational knowledge, insight into related experiments, and operational environments remain important in model-based experimentation. There are also additional dimensions that should be considered when thinking this special case through:

- What tools exist that could potentially describe both the baseline and treatments of interest of the experiment? One of the fundamental principles of experimentation is that one must form a baseline and systematically introduce change. This implies that we can describe the baseline and its behavior. In DoD architecture terms, the baseline is analogous to the "As Is" architecture, and the treatments are potential "To Be" architectures.[2]

- Are there any complete models developed that represent the phenomenon of interest?

- What are the model's assumptions (explicit and implicit)?

• Given the assumptions, what is the valid extensibility of the model? In experimentation, we are extrapolating off of existing knowledge. We need to ensure that the model does not misrepresent the concepts of interest.

Usually, an initial conceptual model supporting an experiment consists of a collection of logical and graphical representations of baseline systems and processes, and the changes to the systems and processes that form the "treatment(s) in the experiment. There are two models of interest in model-based experimentation. The first model is a description of the baseline systems and processes against which the changes will be evaluated. The second is the experimentation conceptual model. It is this model that identifies the components of the MCP that are to be represented and evaluated during the experiment.

For transformation-related modeling, it is important to explicitly consider variables in the physical, information, and cognitive domains (Figure 12-3). Alberts et al[3] discuss in detail these domains and their inter-relationships. How these domains and the activities within them are represented in the models or simulations should be determined as part of the pre-experiment process. The NCW Value Chain (Figure 2-1) describes the role of information in achieving desired effects in an operational context.

During the pre-experiment phase, it is important to identify existing models of the baseline system. Some of them may even be formally validated simulations of the system. These sources should

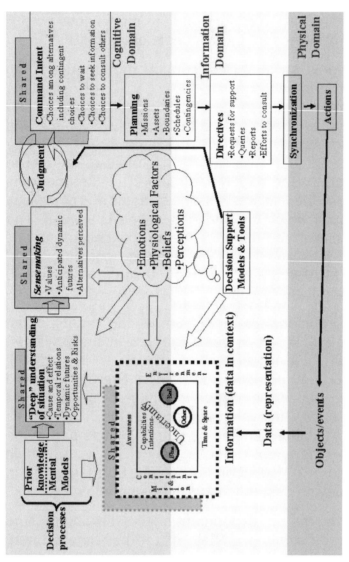

Figure 12-3. Sensemaking Conceptual Framework

be vetted for relevant concepts to be included in conceptual models, as well as potential application in the experiment.

Executable Models (Simulations)

A simulation is simply an executable model. The selection or development of the simulation(s) intended to support a transformation-related experiment is one of the most important activities in the pre-experiment phase. The artificial world being simulated consists of only those components (or abstracts thereof) of the real world and those interactions among those components that are represented in data or in algorithms. There is by definition a loss of information when one reduces the real world to a model. A good model will include both the essential elements and adequate representations of the real world and real world behavior or effects. At an overview level, when thinking about applying constructive simulation tools to experimentation, interactions in the physical and information domains have high potential for achieving insight into cause and effect relationships. Normally, the mapping between the components of interest in the MCP and the simulation components (algorithm and data) is possible. Cognitive domain-related issues can be explored in simulations. However, the exploration of cognitive cause and effect relationships (to generate experimentation data) is often not suited to constructive computer simulation because of the "soft" and complex characteristics of human cognitive processes, like sensemaking.

For transformation-related experimentation, there are some important features to look for in a simulation tool. First, information needs to be treated as a commodity in the simulation. It is important that it be a commodity that can move among simulation entities in either a push or a pull fashion. That is, the command and control algorithms in the simulation cannot assume that perfect information exists in the abstract, and then "reduce performance" based on a simple multiplier. For many transformation-related experiments, this practice reduces to the propagation of an assertion through the simulation. This practice could lead to a misleading conclusion. Network Centric Warfare seeks to reduce and manage uncertainty for commanders and staffs. It does not assert that uncertainty can be eliminated.[4] Therefore, simulations need to address explicitly essential uncertainties. Most important among these are (a) uncertain enemy behaviors (and goals), (b) errors in key sensor systems (false positive and negative), (c) potential errors in the sensemaking process, and (d) potential information infrastructure losses and failures. Third, command and control representations (and representations of information flows) cannot be assumed to be hierarchical, or centrally located. NCW principles seek to recognize and support evaluation of the necessarily distributed decisionmaking that will exist in the future operational environment. Finally, the resolution of the simulation should be consistent with the resolution of the components of the MCP that are the independent variables in the experiment. In the extreme, if one is considering experimenting with the structure of a Standing Joint Force Headquarters, a constructive simulation that explicitly models sensor-to-shooter kill chains is probably inappropriate.

Given the above principles, many existing, "validated" simulations can not effectively support transformation experimentation. Some rules of thumb for selecting or developing useful simulation tools are:

- Do not limit the search to formally validated models. These models may in fact not be valid for transformation concepts;

- Seek to use stochastic models as a default. The "second moment" or variability of outcomes is usually where the catastrophic failures and exceptional opportunities are found. Deterministic models assume those conditions away; and

- Ground the simulation in sound conceptual models of the baseline and modified MCP or MCP component and its behaviors.

Conduct of the Experiment

Let us assume we have selected or developed a simulation to support a modeling experiment, and that we are now ready to use the executable model or simulation to generate the data we need to "collect." We must now carefully consider the design of the experiment (what data is to be collected under what "circumstances." This design must be consistent with the stated hypotheses or discovery objectives. The best information for achieving this consistency is found in the mission capability package and the supporting conceptual models. Complex MCPs in which multiple hypotheses are being tested need to be treated differently from small, focused discovery experiments.

All experiments should be supported by a systematic exploration of the space of interest. This is sometimes referred to as the design matrix. The details of these designs should be grounded somewhere in the rich academic literature that describes specific techniques.[56] For the purposes of this discussion, there are two top-level design concepts with which we should be familiar. The first are designs that capture first order effects. These designs are the simplest and are intended to capture major, direct changes that are attributable to the independent variables. Normally, these types of designs are applicable to limited objective and discovery experiments. An example would be a "Plackert-Berman Design," which was applied in support of Army equipment modernization simulation experiments in the 1990s.[7] This type of design requires fewer runs of the supporting simulation, and the output can be efficiently used in traditional statistical inference approaches. The disadvantages are that the insights are limited to these first order effects. Most MCPs and most operational phenomenology are highly interdependent and nonlinear. There are many experimentation techniques that support the exploration of these complex situations. These should be selected for their fit with the situation the researcher encounters. Factors such as the number of controllable independent variables, suspected complexity of the dependencies, and computational capacity should be considered.

A technique that is rapidly emerging as an effective approach for addressing complex decisions and outcome spaces is exploratory modeling.[8] [9] These techniques support the conduct of experiments that search large combinations of independent and intervening variables and then present the output data in a manner that assists human insight. In fact, this is a technique that might be employed to effectively simulate stochastic modeling using deterministic simulations and large numbers of different input variables.

Post-Experiment Phase

One of the advantages of model-based experiments is that they are potentially more flexible than experiments involving human subjects (particularly large military organizations). So, activities normally associated with the post-experiment phase of an experiment can and should stimulate rapid iteration and evolution of the model, the experiment's design, and expectations. It is this phase of the experiment that should, in most circumstances, be led by skilled analysts. Skilled, energetic inquiry into model behavior and experiment data provided to the remaining members of the experimentation team will contribute to higher-quality results. These results could confirm or refute a priori hypotheses, generate new hypotheses, or cause refinement of the model to support more refined exploration of the hypotheses of interest.

Analysis

In practice, the analysis is iterative with multiple entry points. Figure 12-4 describes this cyclic process in terms of the types of reasoning that should be applied to systematically explore the experiment's results, and its implications with respect to the hypotheses of interest.

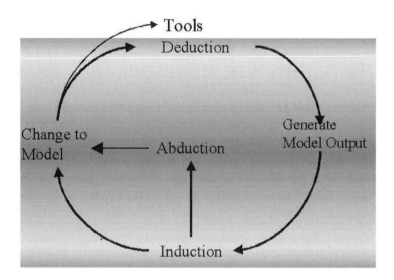

Figure 12-4. Analysis of Model-Based Experiment Results

We will begin discussion with deduction. This is actually accomplished during the pre-experiment and experiment phases when we fully specify the model. Models, including simulations, are deductive tools because all possible behaviors are specified by the input data, including the algorithms. Historically, modeling and simulation were largely limited to supporting deductive approaches to analytical thinking. Emerging computational power, simulation techniques, and inductive tools and techniques provide a previously unachievable foundation for analysis. It is the combination of these capabilities that enables this more robust approach to be applied.

The generation of model output centers on the conduct of the experiment, or the execution of the experiment design. The objective of this stage, as described earlier, is the production of data about the dependent variables.

Model-based experiments, using the techniques described above, will generate significant amounts of data. This data is explored using inductive techniques that generate a fully specified model from the inputs. Examples of such approaches are Bayesian Networks, Neural Networks, and Data Mining. These techniques effectively generate a "meta-model" that describes the relationship between the dependent and independent variables implied by the model.

There are a number of possible conclusions that can be drawn from the "meta-model." It could conclusively confirm the hypothesis, in which case the results could then be used to support more robust experimentation. However, the hypothesis could also be seemingly disproved. The experimentation team in this case could traverse one of two paths. First, it could conclude that the model did not adequately represent the real world and modify the model using the insights that were developed as a result of the experiment. Another possibility is that the insights resulted in the formulation of a new set of hypotheses. That is, a form of abduction occurs and the model is modified to support exploration of the new hypotheses. In both of the cases that result in model modification, the process proceeds back to the pre-experiment phase and structured exploration continues.

Counterintuitive Model Results

Sometimes when analyzing the results of a model, counterintuitive results are encountered. In transformation-focused modeling experiments, it is likely that this will occur relatively more frequently than in traditional analyses using models. Moreover, model-based experimentation best demonstrates its value during the exploration and resolution of counterintuitive results. Achieving those insights requires the skillful participation of the multidisciplinary team.

When a fully-specified model generates counterintuitive results, there are three possible causes. First, the model is wrong. It is incorrectly representing some important element of the real world, and that error is skewing the model's results. These errors should be corrected, and the experiment redone. The second possibility is that the model is correct, as far as it goes, but it is insufficient in its representation of the real world. That is, there is some essential element of the real world system that is missing from the model. This deficiency has situational-dependent responses. If it is possible, the model should be extended to include the omitted features and the experiment should be redone. If it is not possible to address the deficiency within the context of the existing model, then the team should either develop a separate model-based experiment that focuses on the deficient area, or the experiment's report should contain caveats that describe the deficiency and its implications. This documentation can serve to prevent inappropriate conclusions and to help focus future experimentation on the exploration of the issue. The final possibility for a counterintuitive result is that the model is providing an unexpected insight. These potential insights are the most valuable contributions of model-based experimentation. It is these insights that provide new directions for transformation concept development and planning.

Issues in Model-Based Experimentation

Model Validity

DoD Instruction 5000.61 lays out policies and procedures for validating models and simulations. In the case of transformation experimentation, following the letter of this policy can, in fact, be counterproductive. Under the policy, components have the final authority for validating representation of their forces and capabilities.[10] This means that only face validity (credibility to expert audiences) is sound and that it is valued over construct validity (correct identification of the factors at work and their relationships) and empirical validity (the ability of a model to make correct predictions). By definition, exploring transformation involves changing the way forces, headquarters, and support functions are organized and interact. Representations of these experimental concepts in models, although substantively appropriate, may not be consistent with the traditional component view of modeling. Moreover, the administrative timelines and expenses associated with meeting the VV&A requirements are inconsistent with the concept of rapid iteration through discovery types of experiments.

Thinking about validity effectively in the context of transformation experimentation mandates a return to first principles in modeling. One way of organizing validity-related thinking is to recognize three kinds of model validity: technical, operational (tactical), and dynamic.[11]

Technical validity has four primary components:

- *Model validity* - refers to the model's correspondence to the real world (fidelity, or in the language above, this includes some aspects of construct validity);

- *Data validity* - refers to the validity of both raw and structured data. Raw data validity refers to the capacity to capture the phenomenon being modeled correctly or the accuracy, impartiality, and the ability to generalize. Structured data validity deals with abstract data, such as aggregated units;

• *Logical validity* - refers to the way in which model behaviors and results are considered. For example, consider two replications of a stochastic simulation. In one replication, an aircraft carrier is sunk, and in the other it supports the mission at full capacity. But, analysis of half an aircraft carrier is not reasonable. This also refers to the absence of relevant variables. For example, a model of a network-centric concept that assumes perfect communications and perfect sensor performance (again, in the language above, this includes some aspects of construct validity); and

• *Predictive validity* - do the model's results make reasonable predictions of outcome conditions? This is very difficult to confirm for models and simulations of future concepts and technologies. However, the issue should be raised. If a model is generating counter-intuitive predictions or its results appear inconsistent, the modeler will want to investigate the causal mechanisms with the model.

No model meets all of the criteria for technical validity. Therefore, the next step in validation is to assess the importance of the divergence, or evaluate the operational validity of the model. This process should have support and input from all segments of the multidisciplinary team supporting the experiment. In operational validation, the team should explore the outputs of the model and trace the relationships in the model from that output back to the changes in inputs that caused the change. Additionally, operationally-oriented team members should be assessing operational reasonableness (face validity) of the force behaviors implied by the modeling.

Dynamic validation explores the limiting conditions under which the model is valid. There are two facets that should be considered. The first is with respect to the insight it provides into the behavior of a force or concept. That is, experiments should not draw conclusions lightly about the performance of some platform or small unit doctrine changes from a simulation whose entity resolution is at the level of flight groups and battalions. Second, experimentation teams need to explore and understand the limiting conditions of the decisions that the model should reasonably support.

As a matter of practice, the key validation attributes and conditions should be identified as part of the early pre-experiment planning. The team should identify necessary and sufficient conditions that the model must meet to be considered valid for achieving the experiment's objective. The conditions should be presented to leaders as potential sources of risk to the experiment and be revisited periodically as the experiment planning progresses.

Uncertainty

The best practices described above present some techniques to address issues of uncertainty. Explicit consideration of uncertainty is absolutely essential in experimentation, especially transformation-focused experimentation. The systematic exploration of issues of uncertainty is a necessary component of transformation risk management. Model-based experiments are a potentially high payoff approach to exploring uncertainty because of their efficiency and flexibility. Unfortunately, it is also often among the first things to "go overboard" as the experiment planning process reacts to schedule pressures.

Peer Review

The purpose of transformation-related experimentation is to generate new knowledge. Academia has a long-standing tradition of systematic peer review as professional researchers assert they have "created" new knowledge. Model-based experimentation especially requires this type of peer review because these assertions will be made, either for decisionmaking or for further exploration, without the benefit of real world contact.

Unfortunately, many model-based experiments (and studies) have been completed without the benefit of constructive peer review. This often results in two unfavorable conditions. First, there are logical mistakes in the model (it is invalid) that undermine the model's results. Second, the supported community does not trust the model, which could undermine the experiment's results, even if they are technically credible.

Leaders of model-based experimentation teams should explicitly plan for external peer review throughout the experiment. Ideally, this process should remain informal and flexible. This will keep model-based experiments resource efficient.

Conclusion

Model-based experimentation is a necessary component of an experimentation campaign, particularly in the context of transformation experimentation. If carefully integrated into the experimentation campaign and effectively executed, it will make significant contributions in both the efficiency and effectiveness of the DoD's transformation programs.

[1]The NATO *COBP for Command and Control Assessment*. Washington, DC: CCRP. 1998.

[2]*C4ISR Architecture Framework Version 2.0*. Washington, DC: The Architecture Working Group and the Office of the Secretary of Defense. 1997.

[3]Alberts, David S., John Garstka, Richard Hayes, and David Signori. *Understanding Information Age Warfare*. Washington, DC: CCRP. 2001.

[4]*Understanding Information Age Warfare*. p160.

[5]Recommended reading: McBurney, D.H. *Research Methods*. Pacific Grove, CA: Brooks/Cole. 1994.

[6]Recommended reading: Vadum, Arlene and Neil Rankin. *Psychological Research Methods for Discovery and Validation*. Boston: McGraw Hill Higher Education. 1997.

[7]Loerch, Andrew, Robert Koury, and Daniel Maxwell. *Value Added Analysis for Army Equipment Modernization*. New York, NY: John Wiley & Sons, Inc. 1999.

[8]Bankes, Steve. "Exploratory Modeling for Policy Analysis." *Operations Research*. Linthicum, MD: INFORMS. 1993.

[9]Bankes, Steve, Robert Lempert, and Steven Popper. "Computer-Assisted Reasoning." *CSE in Industry*. St Louis, MO: American Institute of Physics. 2001.

[10]*DoD Instruction No. 5000.61. Subject: DoD Modeling and Simulation (M&S) Verification, Validation, and Accreditation (VV&A)*. October 5, 2001.

[11]Schellenberger, Robert E. "Criteria for Assessing Model Validity for Managerial Purposes." *Decision Sciences Journal*. Atlanta, GA: Decision Sciences Institute. 1974. No. 5. pp644-653.

CHAPTER 13

Adventures in Experimentation:

Common Problems and Potential Disasters

Purpose

Transformation has become a major thrust for DoD leadership. As a result, more and more organizations have undertaken campaigns of experimentation to discover, explore, refine, and demonstrate innovative concepts and applications of technology. While these efforts are clearly well-intended, and many have produced valuable insights and knowledge, not all of these efforts have been fully thought through. As a consequence, many experiments have been less productive than they could have been. Similarly, because of a failure to even think about, much less manage, linkages among individual experiments, many past campaigns of experimentation have contributed far less to the body of knowledge than they might have.

This chapter identifies and illustrates the types of problems experienced within the past several years. Looked at with perfect hindsight, some of these errors appear to defy common sense and logic. However, every type of mistake described here has happened to at least two different experimentation teams working within the DoD. Because the purpose of this Code of Best Practice, and this chapter, is to inform and teach, no individuals, teams, organizations, or agencies are identified by name and some effort has been made to mask the identity of the specific experiments from which these lessons have been drawn.

Many of the issues raised here have also been reviewed in earlier sections of the Code where the actions necessary to avoid these mistakes were discussed as being a part of best practice. This section of the Code approaches these issues from the opposite perspective, treating them as errors and discussing the problems that result. We hope that this may help experimentation teams and their sponsors see the importance of thoughtful planning, careful implementation, and specific attention to the issues raised here.

Problems experienced in the pre-experiment phase often prove the most serious because they are difficult and expensive to fix later on and may, indeed, prove impossible to overcome. Unfortunately, they have also proven to be quite common, particularly as DoD organizations, with limited experience and much to learn, have begun to experiment.

Flawed Experimentation Environment

One of the most common problems is the effort to "piggyback" transformational experiments onto training exercises. As noted earlier, training exercises always take place in the context of immediate needs and current doctrine, organization, and training. Moreover, the bulk of the funding in these exercises comes from the training budget. For both of these reasons, experimentation objectives have been subordinated to training objectives. Consequently, genuinely transformational MCPs can almost never be introduced into these venues. At best, specific limited innovations (hardware, software, etc.) are introduced piecemeal. This is no more productive than introducing military forces into a battle piecemeal. Their full potential is simply not going to be realized.

Another common problem is introducing multiple experiments into a single venue, such that they actually *interfere* with one another. Because modern military operations are complex and interrelated, conducting several experiments in the same venue (for example an ACTD or a JWID) opens the possibility that two or more of the experiments actually confound one another. In some cases, this has occurred because one experiment's independent variable was the dependent variable in another. However, the first variable was being consciously manipulated, which rendered the second experiment moot. More commonly, intervening variables important to one experiment (and therefore controlled) are being treated as factors in another experiment, again undercutting the second experiment. Multi-experiment venues need careful and detailed experimentation plans as well as continuous opportunities for interaction between the various participants.

On a similar note, *partial* implementation of developmental technology can have a sudden, disruptive effect on experimentation when not all of the essential supporting functions have been included. Of particular concern in some past experiments has been the lack of adequate logistics and infrastructure support for newly developed systems. By their very nature, advanced technology experiments involve the application of systems that have not gone through a full development cycle. Hence, the ability or inability to support such systems in an experiment can be problematic and disruptive to experimentation events. In other cases, the presence of technical support personnel, sometimes in very large numbers, can introduce artificialities. One of the best strategies for anticipating and minimizing such disruptions is the inclusion of rehearsal events in the experiment schedule.

Advocacy experiments designed to showcase or build an unambiguous body of evidence to support a particular initiative fly in the face of good experimentation practice and *waste precious resources* needed for *genuine* experimentation. This occurs when an organization seeks to prove the value of their concept or system enabler, rather than genuinely researching alternatives. It is often characterized by unrealistic assumptions, scripting red so that the blue approach will be optimized, collecting narrow data on easily controlled topics or other artificialities designed to ensure that the results are consistent with organizational goals rather than knowledge gain.

The failure to allow *intelligent* red in dynamic experiments is a similar error. Many of the most effective U.S. and coalition courses of action involve targeting red's decisionmaking and C4ISR systems – delaying decisions, overloading the systems, or manipulating those systems. However, if the red moves are pre-scripted or significantly constrained, then there is no impact on red C2, regardless of how well the blue approach functions. Moreover, the absence of an intelligent red force means that the U.S. force and C2 systems are not being challenged to be agile.

Reliance on a single scenario rather than capability-based analysis is another problem sometimes encountered. Choosing a single scenario means optimizing blue's approach during the experiment. This fails to acknowledge the fact that the U.S. and its coalition partners are facing an increasingly diverse set of threats and should be relying on capability-based analysis to ensure our future systems are robust and adaptable to the range of possible threats. Moreover, when scenarios are an essential part of an experiment, then a set of scenarios that represents the range of interesting and important challenges is the correct approach. The selection of only a single problem or class of problems is incorrect.

Failure to select *appropriate subjects* can limit the value of an experiment. Most DoD experiments assume that the subjects are competent at their military specialties. However, experiments have been held in which the subjects were partly drawn from groups who lacked the experience and training required to perform the key tasks effectively. When this occurs, performance is more closely associated with subject capability than with the innovations being assessed. The result is an experiment that does not contribute to increased knowledge or understanding.

An earlier discussion stressed the problems associated with *failure to train subjects adequately*. When this happens, performance improves over time as the subjects improve their skills with experience, and thus the data tend to understate the value of the intervention. In essence, part of the experiment is spent training the subjects. Because most experiments train on a schedule and do not give the subjects proficiency tests to see how well they have mastered the interventions being studied, the experimentation team can only make informed guesses about the potential value of the intervention. If proficiency tests are introduced, data analysis can be done that controls for differences in the initial skills of the subjects. If pre- and post-experiment proficiency tests are used, even richer analyses are possible.

Lack of Adequate Resources

For a variety of reasons, *several DoD organizations that "recognized" the importance of performing experiments have not given them adequate resources or priority, or devoted adequate time to the pre-experiment phase*. This is a serious problem and has greatly impacted the value of a number of important efforts. This low priority for resources, planning, and time can result in late creation of the experimentation team, insufficient organization during the pre-experiment phase, failure to identify and organize adequate expertise, failure to have a pool of appropriate subjects, failure to provide adequate training materials or training time for experiment participants, failure to provide an appropriate variety of rich scenarios or drivers for experimentation, and failure to provide enough resources for quality analysis. All other things being equal, most organizations would benefit from only a few well-crafted and properly supported experiments than with more that are inadequately resourced.

All too often, the experimentation teams are too narrow, lacking the skills and experience necessary for success. First, they often leave out the range of relevant disciplines necessary to understand the substantive problems under study, including experience and expertise in research design as well as the "soft" disciplines of psychology, anthropology, sociology, organization theory, and political science. Second, teams often fail to include the interagency, coalition, and international communities that create the setting for most military operations today. Excluding either expertise or substantive context under the assertion that these complicating factors will be addressed later, after mastering the core engineering and military problems under study, is a weak argument. Transformation needs to occur in realistic contexts, not artificially constrained ones. Moreover, human behavior is one of the very real obstacles to success, so it needs to be embraced as a crucial element of the problem.

Flawed Formulation

As the DoD has worked to learn how to experiment, *some teams have generated sets of hypotheses that will not contribute to knowledge maturation.* These are often long, clumsy structures that essentially argue "IF we do lots of things correctly, THEN we will perform successfully." These formalisms are inadequate to guide research, even discovery experiments. They need to be replaced by the simple IF, THEN, CONDITION form introduced earlier in this Code. Formulations also need to be supported by a set of null hypotheses that will guide analysis and permit genuine gains in knowledge.

Another form of weak experiment formulation is *the creation of models so simple that obviously relevant variables are simply ignored.* When the underlying model is "under-specified," the results will be artificial and will lack the robustness needed for transformation. The simplest and most common form of this error occurs when the differences between human subjects or teams of subjects are ignored. Experimentation designs that assume all subjects and teams are identical often fail to generate useful products because their results actually depend on the humans involved. Similarly, failures to instrument in order to record changes in work processes or informal group structures have led to missed opportunities to gain important knowledge. Simulation experiments in which perfect information is assumed also fall into this class of error.

Some recent experiments have not manipulated the independent variable adequately, thus failing to provide the basis for establishing causality. Without variability in the independent variable, it is impossible to show correlation or causality. One of the major reasons for developing a model of the phenomenon under study before each experiment is to ensure that the "interesting" region is understood for the variables of interest. If the range of values the independent variables will take is left to chance, or worse yet, if it is designed as a very narrow range, then the likelihood that major effects are observed in the dependent variables of interest declines rapidly. This can reduce the quality and importance of experimentation results dramatically.

Failure to control for human subjects can also create problems in experiments. One recent experiment that used small groups as surrogates for command centers had the unfortunate experience of having group leaders with radically different interpersonal styles. As a result, the differences in performance were clearly associated with those differences and could not be linked to the innovations under study. Another experiment had serious problems because there was a clear difference in the expertise and knowledge of its teams. Fortunately, this experiment was using a "Latin Squares" design in which each team had equal exposure to each treatment or intervention, so the very obvious difference between teams did not adversely impact the results.

Failure to control for organizational change can also be a problem. Most DoD experiments assume consistent work processes and organizational structures. However, human subjects are remarkably adaptive. More than once they have decided to alter their functional organization in the middle of an exercise. Sometimes they do so in the middle of a single trial. Unless the experimentation team is prepared to capture those changes and to include them as intervening variables in its analyses, the experiment may well miss important findings.

Experiments often lack a baseline or comparative structure. The lack of a baseline or comparison between two meaningfully different alternatives violates a fundamental principle of experimentation. This error has often occurred in transformation experiments involving the introduction of advanced information system technology into command and control operations. The absence of a meaningful baseline (in this case, the absence of this technology) or comparison between alternative approaches makes it impossible to measure the value-added associated with the new technology. As a result, sponsors and stakeholders are left with only anecdotal evidence that the new technology represents a worthwhile return on investment.

Perhaps among the most frustrating problems encountered are experiments that consciously implement only part of a mission capability package. The rationale given is almost always the same – an opportunity existed to try something new, but not enough time or money was available to include the other elements believed necessary to create a real capability. The consequences of these decisions are easy to foresee. At best, the impact of the isolated element will be badly understated. At worst, this isolated element will perform worse than the current or baseline system or approach. Both the greater familiarity with existing tools and approaches and the fact that new tools and technologies imply different work processes, organizational structures, and training mean that thrusting a partial change into an existing system is a very weak approach to transformational experimentation.

Failure to develop an explicit model of the problem and processes under study also makes it very difficult to run a successful experiment or campaign of experimentation. The approach that, "we'll try it and see what happens," almost invariably means that the experimentation team will have an incomplete or erroneous data collection plan. As a result, they will have a very difficult time generating meaningful empirical findings. Even discovery experiments should be supported by a simple model of what the team believes is important and the dynamics they expect to observe. For example, the humans in C2 systems are often very creative in adapting their work processes and even structures as they gain experience with a set of tools or problems. Failure to be ready to capture and document those changes, which are often crucial intervening variables, may mean those changes are missed. At a minimum, it will mean that the same topics will have to be reexamined in another experiment.

Flawed Project Plan

All too often, DoD experimentation is started from a narrow base, or even as though no one else has thought about the subject under analysis. This is enormously wasteful of both time and energy. All experimentation efforts should organize a team to identify the leading researchers and practitioners in any field where research is contemplated. (This is a practice that DARPA, among other research and academic institutions, regularly employs.) This, and a rich review of existing work, are important ways to identify crucial issues, work only on innovations that can matter, and save resources by building on existing knowledge.

As noted earlier, experiment design is a difficult, complex, and dynamic field. While the basic principles are clear, the specific techniques available, and the types of analyses and modeling appropriate to assess experiments are not easy to master. *Failure to expose the detailed research design to peer review* has often resulted in less than optimum use of resources and knowledge gain from DoD experiments. This does not imply that research designs should be circulated widely like experimental findings. It does mean that seeking constructive criticism from a few trusted peers outside the experimentation team will often pay off handsomely.

Failure to develop explicit data collection plans and data analysis plans leads to serious difficulties. Remarkable as it sounds, one of the most visible experiments conducted in the last decade had no formal data analysis plan. The assumption was that "everything" should be captured and the analysts could then figure out what to analyze later. Not surprisingly, serious problems occurred because they had to try to create information relevant to a number of issues that emerged as crucial but had not been foreseen, and the process of analysis took an extremely long time. Another program, in a different agency, proceeded on the assumption that they would recognize what was important and therefore created no data collection plan. They have had great difficulty generating credible results and getting resources to continue their efforts.

Failure to hold a rehearsal is one of the most serious errors an experimentation team can make. Despite a wealth of experience demonstrating that rehearsals and pretests surface problems, thus helping to avoid practical problems that are difficult to foresee when planning in the abstract, some experimentation teams have found that they lack the time or resources for a proper rehearsal. When that occurs, the first several trials of the experiment essentially become the rehearsal. This can mean that important objectives are not achieved, and almost always means that the data from those first several trials will have to be thrown out.

Due in no small measure to the press of events and a legitimate desire to use data from an experiment to support decisions (particularly resource allocation decisions) experimentation results have been rushed. So-called "quick look" reports and "initial assessments" are scheduled days, or even hours, after the end of the experimental trials. This is an appropriate approach when conducting training exercises, but far from useful in experimentation where detailed data analysis is often needed to find what was learned. It is important to note that the empirical data sometimes contradict the impressions of human observers and controllers. When these early evaluation sessions are scheduled, the most readily available data drive the senior leadership's understanding of what was learned. Hence, data generated automatically and survey data from subjects and observers, which can be gathered and processed quickly, predominate. Serious analyses, often involving comparisons of data and information collected in different locations at different times as well as the careful review of the data and searches for anomalies and alternative explanations, typically require weeks and can take months for complex experiments. Moreover, these serious analyses often contradict or condition the data readily available and the opinions of the participants in the experiment. However, the "rush to judgement" has often already occurred, rendering these richer findings and their stronger interpretation moot.

Failure to control visitor access would seem to be an obvious problem, but remains a factor in too many DoD experiments. Military organizations are hierarchies and prominent efforts at transformation activities are often visited by sponsors and senior officials who are trying to understand what is going on and provide support. However, the presence of senior officers or experts will alter the behavior of subjects. Sometimes they become distracted, sometimes they work extra hard and become hyper-vigilant, and sometimes they become nervous. Remarkably, some experimentation teams do not plan for visitor control. One recent experiment was conducted in spaces that had to be transited by those working on an adjacent project. Others have been interrupted by senior officers who wanted to talk with some of the subjects while the experiment was in progress. Still others have invited senior visitors to take a seat and participate in the experiment itself. All these experiments were impacted and, therefore, less useful than they might have been.

Last minute set-up and equipment problems tend to occur as a consequence of not planning ahead. Almost all experimentation involves federations of systems. Even when the IT being used is from a single system, new linkages must be established between the simulation driver and that system, between the system and the automated data collection efforts, and to support experimentation administration. Failure to allow appropriate lead time for bringing these systems online or resources to maintain them and respond rapidly when problems are encountered can disrupt the schedule for experimentation and may corrupt some of the data being collected.

Failure to debrief all participants is a puzzling error. Those involved in an experiment all see the events from different perspectives. All of them should be debriefed so that their insights are available to support understanding of the findings and also because many of the less central participants will know about glitches and anomalies that may not be immediately visible to the senior members of the experimentation team.

Measurement/Analysis Problems

Failure to instrument properly so that the needed data can be collected is all too common. This usually is a consequence of waiting too late to develop the data collection plan and therefore being unable to instrument the computer systems being used or to arrange for proper recording of crucial aspects of the experiment. Failure to instrument properly almost always means failure to capture data properly and reliance on indirect indicators or human observers, reducing the validity of what is learned. This also stems from failure to use a model.

Reliance on "happiness tests" for assessment of objective issues is all too common. Military utility is important and the comments and insights of experienced personnel, subjects, observers, and controllers are all valuable to the experimentation team. However, there is a rich literature that demonstrates that people of all types, despite their best efforts, tend to see what they expect to see. Moreover, several DoD experiments have shown that the opinions of experimentation participants about their performance using specific innovations and their performance measured objectively are very different. Experimentation teams that seek to avoid the hard work of identifying objective measures by relying on simple surveys are very likely to generate flawed results.

Too often, experimental data collection focuses only on what can be easily recorded and measured, rather than on metrics for critical indicators of performance and effectiveness. This type of error is most often observed in experiments involving the introduction of advanced information technology into command and control. For example, considerable effort will be focused on measuring the flow of message traffic among command and control nodes, or on electronically capturing the status of specific situation displays during an experiment. Yet, at the same time, little or no attention will be given to the information content of message traffic or situation displays, the relative significance of this information in the context of the operational scenario, or the impact of this information on the sensemaking and decision processes of a command group. As a result, analysts are left with little empirical basis to judge whether or not the increased distribution of information actually had a positive effect on command and control performance.

Inadequate access for observers has also been a problem in some experiments. Those experiments that depend on human observers always face a tradeoff between keeping them from impacting the data and allowing them access. However, a few experiments have actually been run on the contradictory assumptions that human observers are needed to track the behavior of subjects, but should not have access to decisionmaking or other key activities. In fact, while the presence of observers will impact behavior somewhat, that impact can be minimized by (a) having them present all the time, including subject training and rehearsals, so they "fade into the woodwork," and (b) being certain that the participants and observers understand that they are recording what happens in order to assess the innovation and its impact, but not to evaluate the subjects.

Confusing measures of performance with measures of effectiveness is not a "fatal" error, but it does impact the interpretation of findings. Measures of performance deal with whether systems work. Measures of effectiveness deal with whether it matters whether the systems work. To take a simple example, precision munitions designed to hit targets with very small aim points have "performed well" if they hit those targets. If, however, the weapons carry only a small warhead and therefore do not damage the targets significantly, they have not been effective. The value chain discussed in the section on measures of merit should enable experimentation teams to select the appropriate sets of metrics for each experiment. When possible, these should not be limited to measures of performance, but also include appropriate measures of effectiveness (force effectiveness, mission accomplishment, policy effectiveness, etc.).

Failure to capture anomalous events and time periods can also limit the value of experimentation data. No experiment goes perfectly. Systems being used by the participants break down, subjects become ill and must be replaced by others with less experience on a team, errors are made by controllers, and so forth. As a consequence, some periods of time of performance by subjects will be impacted by factors outside the design. When this occurs, the experimentation team must record the anomaly and make sure that the data from the impacted subjects, teams, or time periods are analyzed to determine whether it is different on variables that matter. If it is, it must be excluded from the main analysis, though it may be examined to see if any useful insights can be inferred from how the anomalous data differ from the main case.

Failure to properly select and train observers and controllers or to maintain quality control on their activities during the experiment will result in poor or irrelevant data. While subject training has been a widely reported issue in DoD experiments, a number of problems have also arisen with observers and controllers. First, these people need substantive knowledge – they need to understand what the are observing as well as the setting in which they are observing it. Hence, the use of academics or graduate students will require training about the experiment setting as well as the substance of the work being performed. People with prior military experience are preferred because they require less introduction. Even so, their experience may well be out of date or drawn from a different perspective than that in use during the experiment, so some "refresher" training is wise. Observers and controllers should also be given training that describes their roles and the behaviors expected from them. Experimentation is an effort to duplicate some aspects of reality, so those involved in conducting experiments need to be as unobtrusive as possible. Remarkably, some controllers schooled in training exercises have been found to try to teach the participants and improve their performance, while other observers have "lent a hand" when the subjects were busy.

Failure to perform inter-coder reliability tests, when human observers and judges must code data, results in data that lacks reliability and credibility. Developing coding rules and maintaining them over time and across several people responsible for converting raw observations into data is very difficult. Social scientists have developed processes over decades of effort to help ensure the data generated are both valid and reliable. Teams that hurry and fail to spend the time and effort to test for inter-coder reliability both after training and during the data coding process itself are vulnerable to both high error rates and "coder drift" as the rules change with coder experience and the types of cases encountered.

Post-Experiment Problems

Data from transformational experimentation are valuable not only to the team that collects and analyzes them, but also for the larger DoD community. First, they are an essential part of the peer review and broad discussion necessary for rich knowledge. Second, they can be of great value for research on related topics. However, *all too often experimentation data are not available beyond the team that collects and analyzes them*. This occurs at times because of classification, though that is rare and should not prevent circulation to others with legitimate need to know and appropriate clearances. It also occurs in an effort to *avoid embarrassing the individuals or organizations participating in the experiment*. However, data can be masked. All too often, holding experimentation data closely for no obvious good reason calls the credibility of the work into question. In every case, failure to keep and circulate detailed results and data slows the effort to acquire better knowledge.

Failure to retain experimentation materials is a related, but less obvious, problem. Experiments, even very simple ones, require a lot of work, much of it in creating the setting and infrastructure necessary for success. Scenarios and vignettes designed to focus experimentation, sets of "injects" intended to manipulate independent variables and create experimentation data, data structures used to drive simulations, linkages between disparate systems to make them function coherently, measurement tools, training materials, video and audio tapes that have already been mined for the data needed in a single experiment, and a host of other experimentation artifacts are potentially valuable to others developing experimentation plans or seeking to replicate important aspects of the experiment. All too often, these artifacts are discarded, disassembled, or not documented, which means they are lost at the end of the experiment.

Issues in Campaigns

Organizations charged with transformational experimentation, whether at the DoD level, within CINCdoms, within Services, or in separate agencies, are very busy and under great pressure to move ahead rapidly. Unfortunately, this has translated, in some cases, into *unrealistic schedules where events start occurring so rapidly that they can neither be managed properly nor used to build coherent knowledge*. While the transformational experimentation agenda is large, progress requires well-conceived, well-executed and tightly linked campaigns of experimentation. Even if they need to be tightly scheduled, failure to provide the resources to fully understand and exploit each experiment and to create schedules that permit the accumulation of knowledge over time are serious errors.

Campaigns of experimentation are, by definition, sets of linked experiments. However, *beyond a common name, some campaigns have not truly linked their experiments together*. That is, they have no real knowledge gain purpose, variables are defined differently, and the outputs from early experiments are not used as inputs to the later experiments. These efforts represent major missed opportunities for improved knowledge.

Unless a model and explicit knowledge repository are created, many of the benefits of experimentation campaigns are lost. *Good campaigns capture and reuse knowledge, sets of scenarios, experimental injectures, measurement schemes, analyses plans, data, and working models. Enormous waste and loss of knowledge occur when these factors are ignored.*

Rather than seeking to accumulate understanding and knowledge, *some experimentation campaigns have sought to create "bake-offs" between competing hypotheses, approaches, or technologies.* This attitude fails to appreciate the likelihood that different approaches and technologies offered within the professional community are more likely to be useful under different circumstances or integrated into a single, coherent approach than they are to be "superior" or "inferior" to one another. Hence, both exploratory and hypothesis testing experiments need to be thought of as crucibles, within which useful knowledge and innovations are tested and transformational knowledge built, rather than as processes of serial elimination.

Conclusions

Perhaps the strongest indication that DoD experimentation remains immature is the inability to recognize the value of permitting "failure." Failure is either (A) a failure to support the hypothesis or novel ideas, or (B) a failure to run a good experiment. Currently, many in DoD will not accept a failure of Type A, but often accept a failure of Type B. This is exactly wrong and a sign that these individuals and organizations do not understand experimentation. This attitude arises from the mindset necessary for military success. However, in many cases, the most successful experiments are those that show what cannot work, the circumstances under which a new system or approach is inappropriate, or how some innovation can be thwarted by simple counter-measures. Learning is every bit as much about understanding what is not true as it is about grasping new insights and knowledge. A real life, positive example of the value of being open to "failure" is JFCOM's concept of Rapid Decisive Operations. After several years of concept development, a number of workshops and seminars to flesh out the concept, and a few experiments to learn how it might be implemented, MG Cash, Director of Experimentation at J-9, was able to tell a workshop that "the word *rapid* may not be right." His organization was not so invested in the concept that they could not learn from their efforts and change the concept while still experimenting with it. This type of knowledge gain is essential if DoD is to be successful in transformational experimentation.

The thrust of this chapter is that there are a great many problems and pitfalls for those seeking to conduct transformational experiments. The good news is that they can be avoided with foresight and planning. This Code of Best Practice is offered as both an introduction to experimentation for those unfamiliar with that process or with that process in the DoD context and also a source of guidelines intended to ensure success.

APPENDIX A

Measuring Performance and Effectiveness in the Cognitive Domain

Introduction

Military experimentation in the past has focused predominantly around the assessment of technology, using traditional measurement approaches from the engineering sciences. Yet, the emergence of concepts such as Network Centric Warfare, Information Age warfare, and effects-based operations have placed increasing importance on how well this technology performs within a more complex socio-cognitive setting. Evidence from the past few years suggests that these traditional measurement approaches have yielded little more than anecdotal insight into how technology and human performance combine in either productive or unproductive ways. Such data, while interesting, does not provide DoD with the quantitative foundation for assessing the return-on-investment of various transformation initiatives. As a result, experimenters have begun to search for more appropriate (and quantitative) methods of data collection that can be usefully applied to addressing performance in the cognitive domain.

To this end, it is useful to address the state-of-practice for quantifying performance in the social sciences. Such methods have matured over the past several decades to provide socio-cognitive research with the same types of statistical analysis and modeling tools used in the physical sciences.

Behavioral Observation and Assessment Scales

Given the "hidden" nature of mental processes, performance in the cognitive domain must be inferred indirectly through behavioral observation or structured interviews. As compared with laboratory experimentation, conducting military experimentation in a real-world setting presents a more complex measurement challenge. In laboratory experimentation, cognitive performance is often reduced to a set of objective measures by limiting the experimental task to a fairly elementary level (e.g., memorize a string of random numbers). In military experimentation, however, participants engage in a variety of extremely complex cognitive tasks for which there are no straightforward objective performance measures. Hence, measurement of cognitive performance in a real-world setting must be built upon an operational definition of the task process and task outcome.

Responding to this challenge, psychologists concluded decades ago that structured methods must be developed for reliably observing different aspects of task behavior and output that were relevant to real-world task performance. Such methods should be capable of assessing both acceptable and unacceptable performance in a way that was amenable to statistical analysis and modeling. Finally, it was recognized that assessment of cognitive task performance is best accomplished by having subject matter experts judge the performance. Unfortunately, subject matter experts are not always readily available to the experimentation team. Additionally, different subject matter experts might not agree on which aspects of performance to focus on or what constitutes different levels of performance. In response to this challenge, a number of behavioral observation methods were developed – initially for use in investigating human error in aircraft accidents, later refined for use in job performance evaluations, and finally broadened to address a variety of dimensions of performance involving humans, technology, and organizations. These methods were designed to capture expert judgments of task performance in the form of a standardized set of quantitative measures.

Two such methods, Behavior Observation Scales and Behavioral-Anchored Rating Scales, are relevant to military experimentation. These methods can be used as direct observation tools during an experiment, or applied via structured interviews after an experiment to quantify important dimensions of performance in the cognitive domain. Behavior Observation Scales (BOS) are simply a checklist of critical (and observable) behaviors that correlate with acceptable task performance. They can be employed during an experiment to provide a quantitative estimate of how many times acceptable task performance occurred in a particular setting. However, a more useful tool is represented in the Behavioral-Anchored Rating Scale (BARS). Here, the experimenter can use a BARS to assess the degree to which some task dimension is performed –typically on a 3, 5, or 7-point scale that extends from unacceptable performance, through minimally acceptable performance, to outstanding performance. At each point along the scale, the levels of performance are "anchored" by detailed descriptions of what type of behaviors might be seen by an observer in a real-world task setting. Compared to the BOS, a well-developed BARS provides more utility for conducting an in-depth analysis of cognitive performance observed during an experiment.

To illustrate these methods further, the following discussion outlines the manner in which a BARS instrument is developed for use in an experiment. Similar concepts apply to the simpler BOS instrument. The procedure for developing BARS is straightforward; however, it includes a number of essential steps:

- Identify a set of critical incidents that exemplify a range of performance in the task area of interest. In this step, the experimenter obtains narrative descriptions of incidents that characterize examples of unacceptable, minimally satisfactory, good, and excellent task performance. These narrative descriptions should pertain to observable aspects of the task performance (e.g., behaviors and output) and should be specific enough to uniquely characterize the level of performance. That is, the descriptions should be sufficiently specific to allow different observers to agree on the level of performance witnessed.

- Cluster the critical events into meaningful dimensions. In this step, the experimenter defines one or more dimensions of task performance that allow the critical incidents to be commonly grouped. This step relies upon judgment informed by a review of relevant research literature.

- Develop a brief, but precise definition of each task dimension. In this step, the experimenter is constructing a framework for observation, assessment, and data collection. As part of this framework, these definitions help to orient the focus of subject matter expert data collectors during the experiment. It is useful for this step to involve some level of review by subject matter experts (e.g., experienced commanders and staff officers) so that good agreement is achieved on defining each relevant task dimension.

- Develop the behaviorally anchored rating scale for each task dimension. In this step, the experimenter typically defines a 3, 5, or 7 point ordinal scale that represents a ranked rating scale for the task dimension. At each point along the scale, example behaviors drawn from the set of critical incidents are used to construct a brief narrative anchor for that level of performance. By providing a narrative description that uniquely identifies each level of performance, the scale anchors serve to calibrate the observation and judgment of the subject matter expert data collectors. As with the previous step, this step should involve some level of review by subject matter experts.

- Train the experiment observers and data collectors in the use of the anchored rating scales. In this final step, the experimenter conducts training and rehearsal to ensure the consistency of observations and ratings among different data collectors. As part of this step, it is often necessary to "recalibrate" the data collectors mid-way through an experiment. This recalibration is needed because repeated observations of task performance can sometimes produce a downward bias in the ratings as data collectors become more sensitized and focused on task error.

Critical Event Framework

While BARS instruments are useful for assessing certain types of observable task performance, their utility is limited for assessing outcome measures in the cognitive domain. The difficulty arises because internal cognitive functions such as perception, pattern recognition, sensemaking, and decisionmaking are not available for direct observation. At the same time, these internal processes are occurring almost continuously throughout many experiments. Thus, a strategy is required for capturing the most significant aspects of cognitive activity during an experiment. One method for organizing the collection of cognitive performance metrics involves the development of a critical event framework. Based on theories drawn from the scientific literature, this framework is an artifact of the experiment and most likely does not exist in the real world. Similar in purpose to BARS, it serves to focus the attention of data collectors on relevant events within the experiment. However, in this case, the critical incidents are often obtained through post-experiment interviews with the participants rather than being observed in real-time during the experiment.

To illustrate this method, consider an experiment in which new technology and procedures are being assessed for improving the collaboration within a command center. Here, the need arises for a measurement framework for assessing the level and quality of collaboration observed during the experiment. Construction of this framework focuses on how certain critical decisions were formulated and made during the course of the operation. Accordingly, one way of defining each "decision event" might be to break it into three basic steps:

- Framing the decision (identifying what problem or anomaly is being addressed by the decision, what constraints and givens are applicable, and which variables are considered relevant);

- Identifying alternative responses; and

- Evaluating the alternative response.

Next, the experimenter develops a rating scale for describing the level of staff collaboration that supported the commander in each of these steps. Here, two BARS instruments might be developed to provide an ordinal scale assessment – one pertaining to the level of participation (e.g., none, one advisor, many advisors) and another pertaining to the quality of interaction (e.g., low—concurrence only, moderate—solicited options, high—debated options).

Finally, the experimenter defines how the BARS will be used in the experiment. One option here might be to conduct a post-experiment interview with the commander and his principal staff advisors to identify the top three to five decisions that shaped the course of the operation. Then, for each decision "event," the experimenter would have the participants assess the level of collaboration using the BARS instrument.

The Role of Statistical Inference in Measuring and Modeling Cognitive Performance

As noted earlier in this chapter, the goal of military experimentation and modeling is to develop an understanding of how specific transformation initiatives relate to improvements in performance and effectiveness. Thus, the analytic purpose of metrics and data collection is to support the process of identifying relationships among specific input and output variables. In the case of many processes in the physical and information domains, these relationships are largely deterministic in nature. Assuming our measurements to be accurate, we would expect to observe precisely the same experimental relationship on one day as we would on another. If the results vary, we look for additional variables or factors that explain the difference and then add these to our model. Scientists do not like unexplained variability, and this approach has worked well in many areas of research – up to a point!

Two problems arise, however, as experiments address processes with greater complexity. First, we might not be able to conceive of enough variable factors to explain all of the variability in the process we are observing. Second, we cannot be sure that our existing metrics accurately reflect the phenomenon that we intended to measure. Thus, despite the best intentions of the research, we are left with a certain percentage of the process variability that we cannot yet explain. So how does one draw conclusions about what was found or not found in a particular experiment? This is the basic challenge facing those who desire to experimentally measure and then model performance in the cognitive domain.

One approach taken by operations research analysts in dealing with this problem has been to traditionally assume away the relevance of cognitive processes and variables. Hence, early combat simulation models often ignored command and control issues or accounted for them by means of simplified mathematical constructs (e.g., Petri nets). As the field of artificial intelligence matured, these mathematical constructs were replaced by predicate calculus ("if then") rule sets in an attempt to model the cognitive logic inherent in certain military decision processes. The problem with this approach, however, is that the size of these rule sets grew tremendously (e.g., over 20,000 rules to describe a battalion headquarters) but still did not adequately "explain" output variability. In other cases, analysts simply defined cognitive processes as a stochastic "black box." Random number generators were used to select outcomes from a range of possibilities so that the internal mechanisms of these processes could be ignored. At the end of the day, however, modelers can only model what can be discovered empirically through experimentation or real-world experience. This brings the discussion back to the question of how to approach the measurement and modeling of cognitive performance.

Over the years, the goal of many social scientists (those dealing with social quantification) has been similar to that of operations research analysts: the measurement and modeling of complex phenomena. The traditional tool for doing this has been statistical inferential methods of analysis. The use of such methods allows the researcher to do three things:

- Estimate the strength of relationship that exists among a set of process variables/factors and the performance/effectiveness outcomes of the experiment. Applied to transformation experiments, this estimate can provide insight as to whether or not specific transformation initiatives have produced a practical improvement in some military task or function. At the same time, statistical modelers can link various estimates of this type together to form a causal path model that predicts how these improvements translate upwards to higher levels of force effectiveness and policy effectiveness;

- Describe the level of statistical confidence one has in estimating these relationships from the limited amount of data collected during an experiment. This level of statistical confidence can be used as an indicator of whether additional experimental trials are needed to assure decisionmakers that the estimated improvement is real; and

- Characterize the degree to which variability in the outcome measure(s) has been "explained" by the different process variables and factors. This characterization provides the experimenter with insight regarding which variables or factors were the most influential in producing the improvement – a particularly useful piece of information when multiple transformation changes are being investigated simultaneously. Conversely, the amount of outcome variability not explained by the experiment is a useful indicator of the degree to which von Clausewitz's "fog and friction of warfare" are still operating.

While a number of simple, nonparametric analysis methods (e.g., Mann-Whitney U Test, Sign Test, and Chi-Square Test) exist for analyzing data, most currently accepted methods of statistical analysis are all based upon an underlying mathematical equation called the General Linear Model (GLM). The general form of this model is

$$y_{outcome} = \beta_1 x_1 + \beta_2 x_2 + \beta_3 x_3 + \ldots + \beta_i x_i + \ldots + \beta_n x_n$$

where,

$y_{outcome}$ = the level of predicted performance outcome,

x_i = the level of the ith predictor variable or factor,

β_i = the estimated linear weight of the ith predictor variable, or factor derived from the experimental data, and

n = number of predictor variables or factors considered.

The GLM provides the experimenter with a method for predicting the level of system performance or force effectiveness ($y_{outcome}$) that results from combining specific levels or values of each of the n predictor variables or factors. These predictor variables/factors can represent either process inputs (e.g., presence of a new information display) or intermediate process variables (e.g., level of collaboration achieved). Obviously, increasing the types of measures collected during an experiment increases the number of terms in this equation and (potentially) improves the quality of prediction.

The model is called "linear" because this estimate is produced by constructing a "best fit" n-dimensional line through a scatter plot of the empirical data collected for each of the variables or factors during each experimental trial. The term "best fit" implies that this n-dimensional line is adjusted until it minimizes the squared sum of error between each estimated outcome point and the outcome actually observed in a given trial. The resulting n-dimensional line is described by the various estimated β_i coefficients that essentially represent the scaling factors for each input variable or factor. The estimated β_i coefficients are normalized so that they can be compared in relative size to provide an indication of which variables and factors impact greatest on outcome.

A number of different manifestations of the GLM have been traditionally used in scientific research. Historically, a special case of the General Linear Model – called Analysis of Variance (ANOVA) - has enjoyed popular use in experimental research. Typically, ANOVA is used as a statistical test to determine if a single input factor – say, comparison of a new information display against a baseline condition – produces a reliable change in performance outcome between two groups of trials. As part of this method, the experimental differences found over each group of trials are used to construct an F-value that can be related to different levels of statistical significance (expressed in terms of the probability that the observed difference in outcome could have been produced by chance). The desire of the experimenter is to achieve an F-value that reflects less than an $\beta=0.05$ probability of chance occurrence (Note: in some instances researchers demand a more stringent value of $\beta=0.01$). Variations of the ANOVA test have been developed by statisticians to account for pre-existing conditions (Analysis of Covariance, ANCOVA), multiple input factors (Multiple Analysis of Variance, MANOVA), and a combination of multiple input factors and preexisting conditions (Multiple Analysis of Covariance, MANCOVA).

ANOVA-type methods have been traditionally used by researchers to justify the academic publication of their experiment findings. However, limitations of these methods are an issue for military experimentation. First, these methods apply only when the input variables and factors are represented as discrete cases, not continuous variables. Second, these methods tell the experimenter only if statistical significance was achieved or not, and do not provide any sort of indicator of the strength of the relationship found. Thus, this method ignores the fact that an experimental finding may be statistically significant (and, hence, publishable in a scientific sense), but not reflect a real practical finding. Finally, as more factors and levels of each factor are considered in an experiment, ANOVA methods can become quite exhausting to employ.

Given the demand for a better analytic tool, interest has grown during the past several decades in a more generalized type of statistical analysis, Multivariate Regression / Correlation Analysis (MRC). This more general form of analysis offers several advantages over the ANOVA methods used in academic research. First, the MRC methodology can accept continuous variables and factors as input, thus permitting more detailed types of measurements in field experiments. Past studies have shown that the results of multivariate regression/correlation analysis generally hold up even when the predictor variables do not exactly meet the rigorous definition of an interval scale or ratio scale variable. Second, the experimenter can employ transformed variables to reflect non-linear relationships (e.g., logarithmic scaling) and "dummy coded" variables to reflect discrete cases or options. This extends multivariate regression/correlation analysis to address more complex relationships among the experimentation variables.

The GLM also provides experimenters with a visible measure of modeling progress. As with the more restricted ANOVA methods, the GLM allows one to estimate the statistical significance of the model – that is, compute the likelihood that the experiment modeling results were produced by random chance. In addition to yielding a prediction model of the form $y_{outcome} = \Sigma \beta_i x_i$, the GLM also provides a measure called the total correlation coefficient, [0<R<1], that reflects the degree of variability of y_{outcom} that has been accounted for in the prediction equation. In practical terms, R^2 provides a direct estimate of the percentage of outcome variability "explained" by the set of n predictor variables or factors considered in the model. For example, an MRC prediction model yielding a value of R=0.75 would imply that the model has accounted for $(0.75)^2 = 56.25\%$ of the outcome variability observed in an experiment. This might suggest that the researchers should either search for additional explanatory measures and/or conduct additional experiments to raise the level of prediction. In this manner, experimentation can use the R^2 metric as a measure of campaign progress or modeling success.

Sometimes the experimenter will collect measures that are themselves correlated. For example, if one measured both the quality of situation awareness and situation understanding in a given experiment, they would expect to find that these two measures are correlated with one another. If they were to then use both measures as predictors of decision quality, they would find that their predictive contributions overlap somewhat. To address this issue, analysts typically employ the MRC modeling approach in a hierarchical fashion – adding various sets of predictor variables and factors to see which combination yields the best prediction equation. At the same time, this procedure allows the analyst to ignore other, redundant variables or irrelevant variables that do not significantly add to the prediction.

Other forms of the MRC model have been developed by statisticians to provide the experimenter with additional tools for exploring and modeling relationships. Among these are the following:

Canonical Correlation This method allows the experimenter to construct a model with multiple types of outcome measures. Canonical correlation is conceptually similar to MRC, except that it examines the prediction of m outcome measures instead of a single outcome measure. Hence, the procedure involves the estimation of two sets of β coefficients, one set for the predictor variables and factors and a second set for the outcome measures. Canonical correlation provides the experimenter with a more powerful tool for predicting operational performance and effectiveness in more complex types of operations –e.g., effects-based operations.

Factor Analysis This method allows the experimenter to explore sets of measures collected during an experiment and to statistically reduce them into a smaller set of composite measures. Using other considerations and background information, the experimenter can then develop interpretations of each composite variable to develop a deeper understanding of the basic functions or constructs operating within an overall socio-technical process. Such analyses assist this stage of experimentation by helping the experimenter to develop more abstract and simpler explanations of how the various transformation variables and factors are combining and interacting to produce improved performance or effectiveness.

Causal Path Analysis Causal path analysis is a straightforward extension of MRC in which the experimenter is interested in constructing a more complex, multi-level process model. As discussed in the last section of this chapter, causal path analysis provides a technique for combining data from a series of experiments, with each experiment addressing a different portion of the overall process

Specialized Analysis Models   Other specialized models exist for specific types of statistical modeling inquiries. For example, discriminant analysis, logistics regression, and probit analysis reflect different methods for classifying outputs. Techniques such as multidimensional scaling offer a method for identifying important underlying dimensions in an n-dimensional data space. Methods such as Kaplan-Meier survival analysis provide a method of predicting time-to-onset of specific outcomes.

In short, there exists a wide range of statistical inference methods for translating experimental data into empirical prediction models. Commercially packaged models such as SPSS (social sciences), BMDP (biomedical sciences), Genstat (agriculture), and Systat (psychology) offer a basic set of linear modeling procedures that are based on community-accepted criteria for achieving goodness-of-fit in the modeling process. As such, these packages offer military experimentation with a robust set of tools quite adequate for investigating first-order relationships. Through the use of transformation functions, these same models can be used to identify a wide range of nonlinear relationships underlying experimental data structures.

Their ease of use, however, is offset somewhat by their limited ability to address more complex modeling issues, such as non-normal distributions, heteroscedasticity, statistical bootstrapping, and cross-validation. Accordingly, statisticians interested in more sophisticated types of analysis are more apt to use general purpose modeling tools such as GLM for data exploration and statistical modeling. At the end of the day, however, the modeling of cognitive processes comes down to what level of empirical evidence decisionmakers are comfortable with in making program and policy decisions. At one extreme, the academic practice of publishing research with relatively low predictability (e.g., $R^2 = 0.4$) is clearly not acceptable for military experimentation and modeling. At the other extreme, expecting empirical modeling to achieve nearly perfect predictability (e.g., $R^2 = 0.9$) is unrealistic given the complexity of human behavior at the individual and organizational levels. In the end, the decision rests upon two interrelated sets of questions – one set that addresses *practical* significance and the other set that addresses *statistical* significance:

- What is the estimated magnitude of the performance/effectiveness increase, and is the size of this increase of practical significance to the military?

- Do we sufficiently understand what influences performance/effectiveness, and has the experimental research accounted for a sufficient number of variables and factors?

Answering these questions requires a combination of good science and good judgment. At some point, the marginal return of conducting additional experiments or modeling investigations is not worth the added time and cost. In some cases, time and attention are better spent addressing new questions and challenges rather than refining our understanding of old ones. But, ultimately, this is a decision that is collectively made by the sponsors and stakeholders within the experimentation community.

APPENDIX B

Measurement Hierarchy

Introduction

Military transformation experimentation should be built upon a multilevel foundation of metrics that (1) acknowledges the contributions of both technical and human performance and (2) traces these contributions up through various casual pathways as they contribute to mission and policy effectiveness. One such hierarchy that has recently emerged from work within NATO research community and the DoD Command and Control Research Program is shown in Figure B-1. This figure depicts nine specific levels at which measurements can be taken to provide insight regarding the impact of specific transformation initiatives.

As one moves from the rudimentary level of technical performance to the higher level of policy effectiveness, it is clear that different types of metrics are required and that different approaches must be taken to observing and measuring outcome in an experiment or analysis. Generally speaking, these differences can be addressed in terms of:

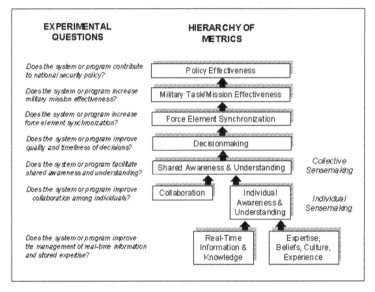

Figure B-1. Hierarchy of Experimentation Metrics

- The context or focus of observation and measurement in the experiment;

- The types of influencing factors or variables that must be controlled or accounted for;

- The basic dimensions by which performance or effectiveness are assessed;

- The timescale or event focus for conducting the observation and assessment;

- The degree of observational transparency that dictates the level of probing and reasoned judgment required for making the assessment; and

• The types of observation and assessment approaches that can be employed either before, during, or after the experiment.

The following sections summarize and compare the each level of measurement in terms of these six issues.

Real-Time Information and Knowledge

At this level, metrics address the collection, storage, movement, and interpretation of reports and sensor data received from the battlespace. Data is transformed into information by placing it in a meaningful operational context. Information is transformed into knowledge by drawing from it relevant conclusions concerning current events, activities, and entities within the existing battlespace. These processes occur at every level within the command hierarchy (e.g., tactical, operational, strategic); however, metrics will typically correspond to that level of command and control of interest in the specific experiment. Figure B-2 summarizes the measurement issues for this level.

Level of Measurement: Real-Time Information & Knowledge		
Observation Context:	Battlespace sensors, reporting systems, communications, information systems, displays		
Factors and Variables to Consider:	*Physical Domain* •Engineering characteristics of equipment •Network connectivity •Network reliability	*Information Domain* •Data formats •Timeliness of data •Completeness of data •Accuracy of data •Availability of analysis and visualization tools	*Cognitive Domain* •Level of expertise of system operators •Compatibility of data formats and structure with mental models of decisionmakers
Dimensions of Performance:	*Physical Domain* •Engineering performance of equipment •Network quality of service during critical periods of the operation	*Information Domain* •Degree to which data are presented in appropriate context	*Cognitive Domain* •Quality of conclusions drawn from information •Timeliness of conclusions drawn from information •Perceptual errors committed
Timescale of Observation:	Typically minutes, but focused during key sensemaking or decision events		
Observational Transparency:	•Physical: High – easily observable during exercise •Information: Medium – requires focused probing during exercise •Cognitive: Low – requires focused probing coupled with expert judgment		
Observation Approaches:	•Automatic monitoring of technical performance + later correlation with critical incidents •Critical incident probes during exercise or as part of post-exercise interviews •Behavior-anchored rating scales, behavior observation scales		

Figure B-2. Measurement Issues – Real-Time Information and Knowledge

Expertise, Beliefs, Culture, and Experience

At this level, metrics address the process of how relevant expertise, beliefs, culture, and experience within the military organization are organized and made available within the command process to transform data into information and information into knowledge. As with real-time information and knowledge, metrics will typically correspond to that level of command and control of interest in the specific experiment. Figure B-3 summarizes the measurement issues for this level.

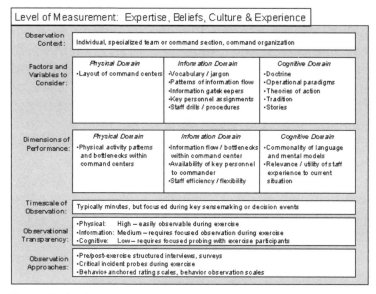

Figure B-3. Measurement Issues – Expertise, Beliefs, Culture, and Experience

Individual Awareness and Understanding

At this level, metrics address the process of individual sensemaking – the integration of relevant military experience and expertise with real-time battlespace knowledge to generate individual awareness and understanding. Awareness can be defined as knowledge that is overlaid with a set of values, objectives, and cultural norms that are unique to the individual, to a community of expertise within the command process (e.g., intelligence, logistics, air support), or to an individual command (in the case of joint/coalition operations). Understanding moves beyond awareness by requiring a sufficient level of knowledge to (1) draw inferences about possible consequences of the situation and (2) predict future states and patterns within the battlespace. Both awareness and understanding uniquely define which conclusions concerning events, activities, and entities within the battlespace are significant or important to a specific individual, a specific community of expertise within a command, or to a specific command. The choice of which individual perspectives are isolated for examination will be a function of the focus and objectives of the specific experiment. Figure B-4 summarizes the measurement issues for this level.

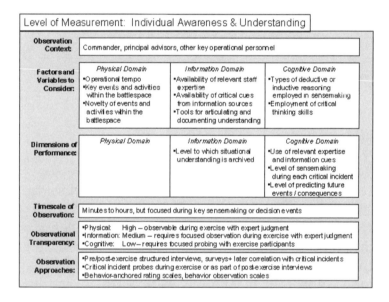

Figure B-4. Measurement Issues – Individual Awareness and Understanding

Collaboration

At this level, metrics address the process structures and mechanisms required to integrate different bodies of knowledge and different perspectives into a relevant common operating picture. These different bodies of knowledge and perspective can exist within a command headquarters or across component commands within a joint or coalition force. Collaboration serves to both (1) reconcile different goals/objectives of the participants and (2) enhance problem-solving capability by bringing to bear multiple perspectives and knowledge sources. Collaboration can take many different forms and be influenced through a number of dimensions, including media, time, continuity, breadth, content richness, domain structure, participant roles, and linkages across which it takes place. Collaboration is necessary because rarely will any single individual or community of expertise be capable of dealing with the complexity of military operations. Figure B-5 summarizes the measurement issues for this level.

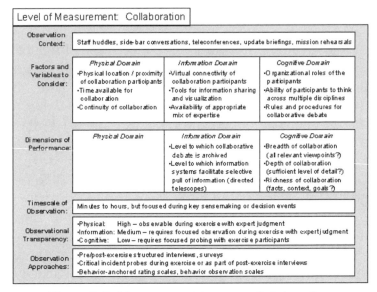

Figure B-5. Measurement Issues – Collaboration

Shared Awareness and Understanding

At this level, metrics address the degree to which the relevant bodies of knowledge and perspectives have been usefully integrated and focused on a common problem or task faced by the organization as a whole. In this regard, shared awareness and understanding are the result of sensemaking extended to the organization level. As the nature of problems and tasks vary over time in a military operation, so will the focus and scope of shared awareness and understanding. Contrary to popular belief, shared awareness and understanding is problem/task-specific and does not imply a universal sharing of all knowledge or experience. Figure B-6 summarizes the measurement issues for this level.

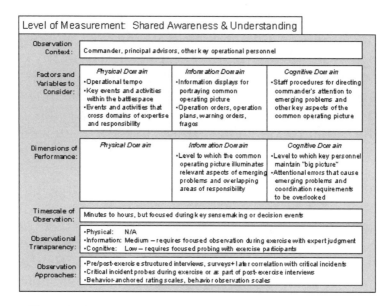

Level of Measurement: Shared Awareness & Understanding		
Observation Context:	Commander, principal advisors, other key operational personnel	

	Physical Domain	*Information Domain*	*Cognitive Domain*
Factors and Variables to Consider:	•Operational tempo •Key events and activities within the battlespace •Events and activities that cross domains of expertise and responsibility	•Information displays for portraying common operating picture •Operation orders, operation plans, warning orders, fragos	•Staff procedures for directing commander's attention to emerging problems and other key aspects of the common operating picture

	Physical Domain	*Information Domain*	*Cognitive Domain*
Dimensions of Performance:		•Level to which the common operating picture illuminates relevant aspects of emerging problems and overlapping areas of responsibility	•Level to which key personnel maintain "big picture" •Attentional errors that cause emerging problems and coordination requirements to be overlooked

Timescale of Observation:	Minutes to hours, but focused during key sensemaking or decision events

Observational Transparency:	•Physical: N/A •Information: Medium – requires focused observation during exercise with expert judgment •Cognitive: Low – requires focused probing with exercise participants

Observation Approaches:	•Pre/post-exercise structured interviews, surveys+later correlation with critical incidents •Critical incident probes during exercise or as part of post-exercise interviews •Behavior-anchored rating scales, behavior observation scales

Figure B-6. Measurement Issues – Shared Awareness and Understanding

Decisionmaking

At this level, metrics address the process of translating understanding into action – all within the framework of the mission/task goals and objectives articulated in command intent. While the general dimensions of quality and timeliness apply to decisionmaking, there exist other important characteristics that can be measured in an experiment. For example, decisions can be arrived at through a number of different socio-cognitive strategies, depending upon (1) time available, (2) the degree of situation recognition that derives from past experience, and (3) the nature of situational ignorance (e.g., too much/little information, too many/few explanatory frameworks). Thus, it is important to address whether or not the organization has appropriately adapted its decisionmaking procedures to these factors – a measure of organizational agility or flexibility. At the same time, it is also important to measure the recursive impact of decisionmaking on the sensemaking activities of the organization. In this sense, decisions are seen to not only lead to actions within the battlespace, but also to the focusing and direction of command staff attention and perspective. Finally, it is important to recognize that many decisions will impact simultaneously on operations at the tactical, operational, and strategic level, as recently demonstrated during operations in Kosovo. Hence, metrics at this level must address this simultaneity of impact, as appropriate, in relation to the focus and objectives of the experiment.

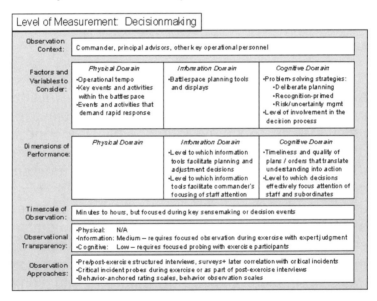

Figure B-7. Measurement Issues – Decisionmaking

Force Element Synchronization

At this level, metrics address the degree to which specific military functions and elements (e.g., reconnaissance and surveillance, information operations, maneuver/assault, logistics, civil affairs) are coordinated to achieve the desired operational effects with maximum economy of force. Because the focus at this level is on operational effects (e.g., combat force attrition, infrastructure damage, area denial, point target destruction, information denial, civilian population management, humanitarian relief), it is important that the metrics accurately reflect the consequences of each effect in the physical, information, and cognitive domains of interest. Synchronization is a multi-dimensional phenomenon. Hence, metrics at this level must address synchronization from a variety of perspectives such as (1) coordination/harmonization of component goals and subtasks, (2) coordination of schedules/ timing, (3) geographic coordination, and (4) coordination of contingency actions taken in response to emergent situations. Synchronization also assesses the level of military force maturity by illuminating the degree to which joint operations have evolved from the strategy of simple deconfliction of force elements to the strategy of creating synergistic effects among force elements. Figure B-8 summarizes the measurement issues for this level.

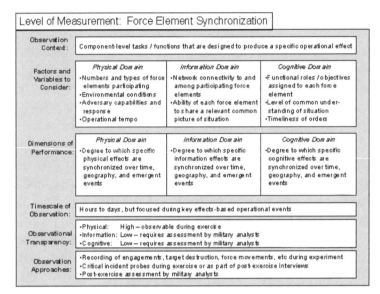

Figure B-8. Measurement Issues – Force Element
Synchronization

Military Task / Mission Effectiveness

At this level, metrics address the degree to which the operational effects combine within a military campaign to achieve the desired end-state or impact on the adversary's will and capabilities. Thus, success at this level of measurement is highly scenario-dependent and is influenced not only by U.S. force capabilities, but also by the capabilities of the adversary, the presence of third-party interests, the geographic region of operation, and the stated goals and objectives of the military task or mission. In addition, the relative contribution of different weapons systems, command and control systems, doctrine, training, leadership and other transformation elements will vary according to these same factors. As with synchronization, metrics at this level are multi-dimensional and must be capable of addressing the consequences of the military task or mission in terms of the physical, information, and cognitive domains of interest. Figure B-9 summarizes the measurement issues for this level.

Level of Measurement: Military Task/Mission Effectiveness		
Observation Context:	Overall operational capability of the adversary, as it is impacted by blue force operations		
Factors and Variables to Consider:	*Physical Domain* •Blue/red force capabilities, including asymmetric options •Environmental conditions •Other players and entities within the battlespace	*Information Domain* •Relative degree to which blue force synchronization and agility exceeds that of red force	*Cognitive Domain* •Goals, objectives and values of blue force •Goals, objectives and values of red force •Goals, objectives and values of other players / entities
Dimensions of Performance:	*Physical Domain* •Achieved degradation of adversary's physical assets by destruction / other means •Timeliness of operation •Blue force losses, including fratracide	*Information Domain* •Achieved degradation of adversary's command and control networks	*Cognitive Domain* •Likelihood that the level of achieved degradation will cause the adversary to withdraw from military campaign
Timescale of Observation:	Days to weeks, but focused during key operational events within the military campaign		
Observational Transparency:	•Physical: High – observable during exercise •Information: Low – requires assessment by military analysts •Cognitive: Low – requires assessment by military commanders		
Observation Approaches:	•Recording of engagements, target destruction, force movements, etc during experiment •Critical incident probes during exercise or as part of post exercise interviews •Post-exercise assessment by senior military analysts and commanders		

Figure B-9. Measurement Issues – Military Task / Mission Effectiveness

Policy Effectiveness

At this level, metrics address the interaction of military tasks and missions with other instruments of national security policy (e.g., diplomacy, politics, humanitarian relief, economic assistance, legal/ justice). Policy effectiveness corresponds with the emerging concept within DoD of effects-based operations – as characterized within recent counter-terrorist operations against al-Qaida and other international terrorist groups. This level of measurement represents a potentially complex challenge because of the often subtle manner in which these instruments combine to produce coercion and influence against an adversary. Thus, metrics must be capable of reflecting the degree of deconfliction, cooperation, or synergy present when military operations are combined with other instruments to achieve specific policy goals. At the same time, metrics at this level must reflect a number of real-world considerations that impinge upon the military operations –e.g., the presence, contributions, and conflicting goals of coalition partners, private-voluntary relief organizations, non-governmental organizations, and transnational organizations in the battlespace. Figure B-10 summarizes the measurement issues at this level.

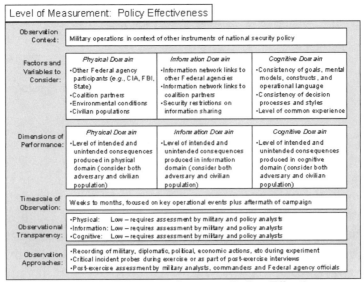

Figure B-10. Measurement Issues – Policy Effectiveness

APPENDIX C

Overview of Models and Simulations

Introduction

A model is defined to be a physical, mathematical, or otherwise logical representation of a system, entity, phenomenon, or process.[1] Conceptually, military experiments use models of postulated future military situations to support the full range of experimentation types, including discovery, hypothesis testing, and demonstration experiments. Simulations are defined as the process of designing a model of a real-world system and conducting experiments with this model for the purpose either of understanding the system or of evaluating various strategies (within the limits imposed by a criterion or set of criteria) for the operation of the system.[2]

In considering modeling and simulation (M&S) "Best Practices" to support experimentation, users should always bear in mind that "all models are wrong. Some are useful."[3] The discussion in this chapter is intended to help members of multidisciplinary experimentation teams better understand models, and guide them through the process of selecting, applying, or possibly developing models and simulations to support the experimentation process. The overall goal is to increase the likelihood of having "useful" models.

Models can be as simple as conceptual flow charts of decision processes, or as complex as large force-on-force combat simulations executing many thousands of lines of software code. Models at both ends of this spectrum can and should be used throughout the experimentation process. An emerging concept in the DoD experimentation, testing, and acquisition communities that reinforces this point is called the model-experimentation-model paradigm.

In order to use models successfully in experimentation, model(s) should meet three basic tests:

- Models must be clearly defined. The experimenter must be able to determine what is (and is not) being described in the model(s) quickly and unambiguously.

- The contents of models must be logically consistent. The logic, algorithms, and data that describe the phenomenology of interest must be compatible. If this is not true, the "answer" the model and accompanying analysis generate could be incorrect or misleading. Seemingly simple inconsistencies can potentially have catastrophic consequences, especially in warfare.

• Models must be transparent. When models are applied and begin generating results, transparency allows team members to better interpret model behavior, identify cause and effect relationships, and obtain insights. This is especially important in C2 experimentation because emerging network-centric doctrine and enabling technologies may result in some counterintuitive outcomes that will require exploration.

Overview of Models and Simulations

The different professional disciplines that are involved in modeling and simulation have subtle but fundamental differences in the meaning of field-specific terms. There is no "right" answer in relation to these differences. It is important, however, that those involved in a particular experimentation effort reach a clear and common understanding of terms and the implications of those terms.

Types of Models

There are many taxonomies in different professional communities categorizing different types of models. This discussion addresses predominantly descriptive models, and draws a distinction between static and dynamic models. Descriptive models focus on providing insight into how a system is, or how it behaves. Static models emphasize the logical, physical, or conceptual layout of a system. These models focus on the system's components, their relationships, and their interactions. Examples of relevant static models are:

- Static Conceptual models - IDEF XX, and the DoD Architecture Framework; and

- Dynamic models (simulations) - which introduce the notion of time, and explore the behavior of the system as the components interact. (Examples include colored petri nets, executable architectures, systems dynamics models, and combat simulations.)

Models and simulations are idealized representations of systems (or networks of systems). Good models capture the essential properties and facilitate insight into the system. An important consideration in developing models of complex systems is the identification of what are the "essential properties" of the system. These will be situation dependent, and should be carefully aligned with the goals of the experiment.

Static Models

Descriptive static models describe how an entity or system is designed, or is expected to behave. One broadly applied static model is the DoD Architecture Framework. The products in the DoD Architecture Framework are an excellent example of how different communities involved in experimentation have differing views of "essential properties." The operational, system, technical, and architectural views of a modeled military system all provide different views of the same thing. As a matter of practice, it is essential that the different views be consistent, balanced, and appropriately resolved to support an experiment.

A conceptual flow chart is another specific example of a simple static model. These models can be used quickly and easily to depict important physical and informational relationships that might exist in the system. Figure C-1 is an example of a conceptual flow chart that shows the linkage models of information value in a command and control system. These models are most useful early in the experimentation process to support early concept development, and to communicate complex concepts to stakeholders that may not be familiar with overall concepts. Their strength is their simplicity. They are domain independent, can be developed with minimal resources, and are straightforward to understand. The weakness of conceptual flow models is in their limited extensibility. As concepts and the supporting models become more complex, these types of models can become unwieldy and confusing.

IDEF type modeling is a logical extension of simple conceptual models, and a possible next step once the limits of a simple model are reached. IDEF diagrams have syntactical and structural rules that allow the models to represent more complex systems clearly than straight graphical models.

A supplemental feature of IDEF models is an ability to be constructed hierarchically. A single node can contain another network that describes the process in more detail. IDEF models are best suited to refining

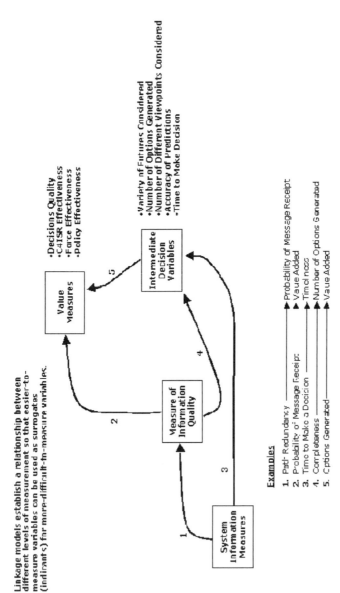

Figure C-1. (from *Understanding Information Age Warfare*)

operational concepts early in the discovery phase of experimentation.

Dynamic Models (Simulations)

Dynamic models, or simulations, are logical or mathematical abstractions of a "real" system that describe, explain, and potentially predict how "real" systems will behave over time. Within the context of experimentation, it is useful to think about three categories of simulations:

- Live simulation - These use human role players interacting with actual or postulated C2 systems within some artificial scenario. Field Exercises are an example of a live simulation.

- Virtual simulations - Sometimes referred to as "human-in-the-loop," these simulations provide automated players and forces that interact with live subjects. The JTASC Confederation is an example of a virtual simulation.

- Constructive simulations - These are closed form simulations designed to run a scenario or set of scenarios end-to-end without human intervention. JWARS, ITHINK, and executable process models are examples of constructive simulations.

Constructive Combat Simulations

Most "standard" constructive combat models in the DoD were designed and developed during the Cold War. They are attrition-based, usually have only limited ability to realistically represent maneuver, and only rarely consider information flows in relation to command and control. Because of this, these models have very limited utility in support of experimentation (and analysis) in support of transformation. These simulations can be used effectively to provide context for some experiments. For example, a simulation describing strategic flow could give first order estimates on force arrivals in support of a game.

There are some ongoing large constructive simulation development efforts that hold some promise for experimentation. JWARS represents explicitly the operation of key sensor systems, flow of information, and operational command and control. The algorithms provided for use in the simulation have been (or are in the process of being) validated by the services. That said, it is a complex tool that is still immature, and has limited scenario data. JWARS would be an appropriate tool to support large-scale wargames, and to provide context for more localized experiments. It is too resource-intensive for early discovery experiments, and focused hypothesis testing.

Executable Architectures (Process Models)

A quickly emerging and maturing class of simulation development environments are called process modeling tools. These tools allow one to rapidly prototype a model of a C2 concept, and then to execute simulations of how that operational concept might behave. Commercially available tools such as G-2 / rethink, Extend, and Bona Parte are already in use throughout the M&S and experimental communities. The advantages of these tools are that they allow rapid prototyping, and are resource efficient compared to live or virtual simulation techniques. These tools are very appropriate in support of discovery and early hypothesis testing types of experiments. The graphical features allow domain experts to work more directly in the model development and analysis process. A disadvantage is that the models produced are often "one of." Therefore, their quality control can vary greatly, and can be problematic to V&V in accordance with the DoD instructions.

Agent-Oriented Modeling

Agent-Oriented Modeling is an increasingly popular subtype of the constructive simulation technique that allows for entities to act (and interact) as "independent actors" in a simulated environment. The description and representation of the C2 process through agent modeling and programming techniques is a distinguishing feature. Modeling of the C2 process as a group of agents, based on artificial intelligence concepts, favors the modeling of the cognitive nature of command tasks. Agents can be implemented, in an object-oriented environment, as either objects (e.g., actor or "applet" type of agents) or aggregates of objects (coarse-grain agents). Such agents interact with each other through a messaging infrastructure. The term *agent-oriented modeling* is used as a way of capturing this idea.

Modeling and Simulation Infrastructure (Engineering)

A number of new and innovative approaches to simulation and information systems allow different objects to be brought together to represent the complete command process, rather like Lego™ bricks. Such a philosophy also encourages the development of models based on holistic and evolutionary principles. Figure C-2 provides a conceptual description of the existing and emerging components that might be used to accomplish M&S in support of experimentation.[4] It is presented as a reference to guide the development of ongoing M&S activities and experiments.

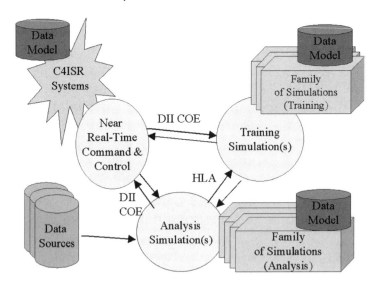

Figure C-2. Infrastructure to Support Modeling, Simulation, and Experimentation

The conceptual infrastructure contains three types of nodes (components). The first is actual or postulated command and control systems. These allow domain experts to serve as subjects and behave as realistically as possible under experimental conditions. The second node consists of high-resolution virtual simulations and more traditional training simulations. These simulations, such as the JTASC training confederation (JFAST) or the emerging JSIMS simulations, often provide the context that stimulates the C2 systems and adjudicates interactions among entities. Finally, the infrastructure contains constructive, or analysis, simulations. The data repositories indicate that all of these tools should be populated with consistent data (See Chapter 9).

There are two specific types of links identified to connect the components. The first, the DII COE, provide a set of standards that facilitate meaningful communication between the different types of applications identified in the nodes. Similarly, the HLA provides a conduit and set of standards that facilitates communications between simulations.

Model "Translators"

Recent advances in the state-of-the-art of modeling and simulation support systems that have tremendous potential to support experimentation are model translators. There are commercial and GOTS tools emerging that allow analysts and engineers to develop different, but consistent, views of the same system. The use of translators can facilitate consistent views between static and dynamic models of systems.[5]

Linking of Performance Models to Effectiveness Models

One approach to using the infrastructure described is to create a structured hierarchy of models and an audit trail from C2 systems, processes, and organizations to battle outcome. The objective is to create supporting performance level models of particular aspects of the process (e.g., communications, logistics) which can be examined at the performance level. These supporting models create inputs to higher level force-on-force models. This ensures that the combat models themselves do not become overly complex.

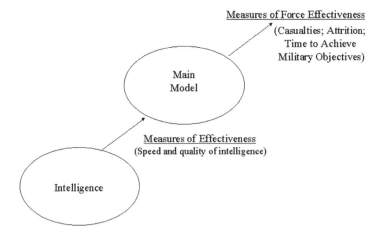

Figure C-3. Model Hierarchy

For example, a detailed model of the intelligence system can be very complex, if we wish to take into account the flow of intelligence requirements, taskings, collection processes, fusion processes, and intelligence products. In order to analyze the impact of intelligence, it is important to have all of this detail, but it does not necessarily have to be represented explicitly in the main model. A supporting model that captures all of this detail can be created in order to produce outputs at the measures of effectiveness level, such as speed and quality of intelligence. These can then form inputs to the main simulation model. The main model then takes these into account in producing its own outputs. These will now be at the measures of force effectiveness level. Examples include friendly casualty levels, adversary attrition, and time to achieve military objectives.

C2 Modeling Guidelines

A general set of C2 modeling guidelines based on a set of requirements should be reviewed by the experimentation team and may be a good candidate for peer review. The primary objective of these guidelines is to relate C2 processes and systems to battle outcome. In order to do this, a model must be capable of explicitly representing the collection, processing, dissemination, and presentation of information. These capabilities, therefore, lead to the set of C2 modeling guidelines described below. It should be noted that these requirements are not yet fully satisfied by any existing model.

These guidelines should be considered part of the model selection and development processes for a specific problem. The experimentation team should be conscious about an explicit or implicit implementation of the consideration points. The C2 modeling guidelines, as presented in the NATO *COBP for C2 Assessment*, include:

- Representation of information as a commodity. This consideration is the most critical and difficult to implement, but is the foundation for the other guidelines, as well as for the model itself. Information should be considered as a resource that can be collected, processed, and disseminated. It includes information about both adversary and friendly forces, as well as environmental information such as weather and terrain. Information should posses dynamic attributes such as accuracy, relevance, timeliness, completeness, and precision. These values should affect other activities within the model, to include, when appropriate, combat functions;

- Representation of the realistic flow of information in the battlespace. Information has a specific source, and that source is usually not the end user of the information. A requirement exists, therefore, to move information from one place to another. Communications systems of all forms exist to accomplish this movement. These systems can be analog or digital. Information can be lost and/or degraded as it flows around the battlespace. The model should represent the communications systems and account for these degradation factors as it represents information flow;

- Representation of the collection of information from multiple sources and tasking of information collection assets. This guideline applies equally to adversary and friendly information. For the collection of adversary information, the model should represent a full suite of sensors and information collection systems, and the ability of these systems to be tasked to collect specific information. For the collection of friendly information, this consideration is just as critical. Knowledge of one's own capability in combat, as well as that of the adversary, is essential for effective decisionmaking;

• Representation of the processing of information. Information is rarely valuable in original form and must be processed in some way. Typical processing requirements include filtering, correlation, aggregation, disaggregation, and fusion of information. These processes can be accomplished by either manual or automated means. The ability, or inability, to properly process information can have a direct bearing on combat outcome;

• Representation of C2 systems as entities on the battlefield. C2 systems perform information collection, processing, dissemination, and presentation functions. They should be explicitly represented as entities that can be targeted, degraded, and/or destroyed by either physical or non-physical means. Additionally, the model should account for continuity of operations of critical functions during periods of system failure or degradation;

• Representation of unit perceptions built, updated, and validated from the information available to the unit from its information systems. This is a critical requirement. Each unit should have its own perceptions, gaining knowledge from superior, subordinate, or adjacent units only when appropriate;

• Representation of the commander's decisions based on his unit's perception of the battlefield. Each unit should act based on what it perceives the situation to be, not based on ground truth available within the model. When a unit takes action based on inaccurate perceptions, it should suffer the appropriate consequences; and

• Representation of IO for combatants. With information so critical to combat outcome, the model should be able to represent the deliberate attack and protection of information, information systems, and decisions. This applies to all sides represented in the model.

Issues in C2 Modeling

This section addresses the core problem of analyzing the effectiveness of C2-related systems, and what it is that sets it apart from other types of operational analysis. The problem lies in making a properly quantified linkage between C2 measures of policy effectiveness, such as communication system delays, C2 measures of effectiveness, such as planning time, and their impact on higher level measeures of force effectiveness, such as friendly casualties, attrition effects, and time to achieve military objectives, which capture the emergent effects on battle outcome. These higher level MoFE are required in order to be able to trade off investment in C2 systems against investment in combat systems such as tanks or aircraft. At present, there is no routine way of making this linkage. Hence, all analyses of C2 systems demand a high level of creative problem structuring and approach to overcome this challenge.

Other modeling issues that have proved important to C2 analysis are:

- Representation of human behavior: rule-based, algorithmic, or "human-in-the-loop;"

- Homogeneous models versus hierarchies/ federations;

- Stochastic versus deterministic models;

- Adversarial representation;

- Verification, Validation, and Accreditation (VV&A); and

- The conduct of sensitivity analysis.

Representation of Human Behavior: Rule-Based, Algorithmic, or "Human-in-the-Loop"

In developing models that represent C2 processes, most approaches (until recently) have been founded on the artificial intelligence (AI) methods of expert systems. These represent the commander's decisionmaking process (at any given level of command) by a set of interacting decision rules. The advantage of such an approach is that it is based on sound artificial intelligence principles. However, in practice it leads to models that are large, complex, and slow running. The decision rules themselves are, in many cases, very scenario dependent and, as noted earlier, human factors and organizational expertise may be needed on a project team to treat these issues correctly.

These factors were not a problem during the Cold War. There was sufficient time to complete extended analyses, and only one key scenario dominated. However, in the post-Cold War environment, such certainties have evaporated. Indeed, *uncertainty* is now an even more key driver in analyses. There is an increasing requirement to consider large numbers of scenarios and to perform a wide range of sensitivity analyses. This has led to a requirement for 'lightweight,' fast running models, that can easily represent a wide range of scenarios, yet still have a representation of C2 which is 'good enough.' Some authors have begun to explore advanced algorithmic tools based on mathematics such as catastrophe theory and complexity theory. This is discussed below under new methods.

Many analyses employ human-in-the-loop techniques in order to ensure realistic performance or to check assumptions and parameters. However, human-in-the-loop techniques are expensive and require the inclusion of soft factors and their attendant Measures of Merit. The introduction of human factors also raises the level of uncertainty as these factors are difficult to integrate and are not necessarily well understood in the C2 specific context. The increased cost, complexity, and uncertainty of human-in-the-loop requires analysts to use these techniques for small portions of the overall problem structure, rather than as the primary analytical method. However, much transformational experimentation will require human-in-the-loop simulations, whether live or virtual.

Homogeneous Models Versus Hierarchies/ Federations

In order to establish the audit trail referred to earlier (tying individual C2 systems, processes, and organisations to battle outcomes), all the detailed processes involved, such as the transmission of communications across the battlefield and the impact of logistics on decisionmaking, should be represented explicitly in a simulation. In this example, the question then arises as to whether all the transmission media (radio, satellites, etc.), with their capacities, security level, communications protocols, etc., should be represented in the main model explicitly, or whether this aspect should be split out as a supporting model of the overall process. Similarly, the detailed logistics modeling required to establish constraints on decisionmaking could be undertaken as part of the main model or in a specialized supporting model. These supporting models could be run off-line, providing sets of input data to the main model (giving rise to a model hierarchy) or they could be run in real time interaction with the main model (giving rise to a model federation). In the off-line mode, the main model would generate demands on the communications and logistics systems. The supporting models would check whether these demands could be satisfied. If not, communication delays and logistics constraints in the main model would be increased, and the main model rerun. This would have to be done a number of times to bring the main and supporting models into balance. However, such an approach can generate valuable analytical insights. The high rate of services that may be required to support the main model can involve a long analysis process. This method becomes critical with a large assortment of C2 parameters or a long scenario period. Sensitivity analysis requirements may also contribute to the requirements for implementation of this approach.

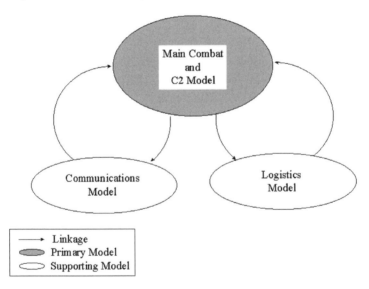

Figure C-4. Illustrative Model Linkage

Figure C-4 shows the main model producing (in addition to its MoFE) a set of dynamic demands on communications (such as communications systems capacity as a function of time) and logistics (demands for transport and key consumables) processes in order to achieve the assessed levels of MoFE. These are then fed back into detailed models of the communications and logistics infrastructure. Those supporting models can then match the dynamic demand placed on the communications and logistics infrastructure to the available capacity. If there is a mismatch, the assumptions in the main model are adjusted iteratively to bring the two models into balance. This approach is more flexible and reactive for a large set of C2 assessments. Nevertheless, the main disadvantage arises from the complexity of the architecture itself (number of linked sub-processes, failure of the sub-model, etc.).

A similar approach can be applied to concepts of operation. In some models, it is possible to describe a concept of operations as a sequence of standard missions (e.g. attack, defend, move). These missions can then be analyzed to determine the demand that they place on the supporting infrastructures. Then, as before, this can be tested offline to see if the infrastructure can cope. Again, this would have to be iterated a number of times, but leads to an ability to relate the infrastructure capacity to its ability to support a defined concept of operations (and hence battle outcome). In addition to the use of such hierarchies of supporting models in an off-line mode, it is possible to create real-time federations of such models to represent, inter alia, combined or joint operations.

Stochastic Versus Deterministic Models

The ideas of chaos theory show that structural variance (or 'deterministic chaos') can occur when sets of decision rules interact in the simulation of a dynamic process. Small changes in initial conditions can lead to very different trajectories of system evolution. Any simulation model of combat, with a representation of C2, has to confront this kind of problem. The merits of a deterministic approach are reduction of run times and the creation of a single 'thread' connecting the input data and the results, making analysis of the model output potentially easier. However, the representation of the C2 process (whether using decision rules or not) gives rise to a number of alternative decision options at a given moment, and can thus potentially give rise to such 'deterministic chaos'. If such effects are likely to arise, one solution is to use stochastic modeling. The use of stochastic sampling in the model, together with multiple replications of the model, gives rise to a *distribution* of outcomes which is much more resistant to such chaotic effects.

Representing Adversary Forces

Historically, adversary capabilities and behaviors were often fully scripted or heavily constrained. This was more appropriate in Cold War contexts than it is today. However, it was never ideal for C2 analysis because the dynamic interaction between friendly and adversary forces is a critical element of C2 representation. Today, much more robust adversary capabilities are employed and indeed are necessary. Analysts must consider not only a range of scenarios, but also the range of possible adversary actions and reactions.

Verification, Validation, and Accreditation (VV&A)

VV&A has traditionally been a challenge for model development efforts, but is particularly challenging for C2 modeling. This is due to the variability inherent in most C2 processes, especially those that involve the human aspects of information processing and decisionmaking.

---

[1]"A Glossary of Modeling and Simulation Terms for Distributed Interactive Simulation (DIS)." August, 1995.

[2]Robert E. Shannon. *Systems Simulation the Arts and Science*. Prentice-Hall, 1975.

[3]George E.P. Box. "Robustness is the Strategy of Scientific Model Building." *Robustness in Statistics*. eds., R.L. Launer and G.N. Wilkinson, 1979, Academic Press, p. 202.)

[4]"Evolving the Practice of Military Operations Analysis." *DoD Applying Knowledge Management*, MORS Symposium. March 2000.

[5]"Executable Architecture for the First Digitized Division." Paul C. Barr, Alan R. Bernstein, Michael Hamrick, David Nicholson, Thomas Pawlowski III, and Steven Ring.

APPENDIX D

Survey

Situation Awareness Questions

Part 1 (Unprompted)

Summarize your assessment of the situation.

Part 2 (Prompted)

1. What is the friendly mission?

2. What are the friendly opportunities?

3. What are the risks to friendly forces?

4. What are the adversary's vulnerabilities?

5. What are the adversary's intentions?

6. What are the adversary's defensive capabilities?

7. What are the adversary's offensive capabilities?

8. If you are unsure of adversary's intentions, what are the different possibilities?

9. What are the important environmental factors in this situation?

Note: There were other questions on the survey form, but the above were the questions used for determining the situation awareness scores.

Acronyms

A

ACTD - Advanced Concept Technology Demonstrations

AIAA - American Institute of Aeronautics and Astronautics

AIDS - Acquired Immune Deficiency Syndrome

APS - American Psychological Society

ATD - Advanced Technology Demonstration

ATO - Air Tasking Order

C

C2 - Command and Control

C4ISR - Command, Control, Communications, Computers, Intelligence, Surveillance, Reconnaissnce

CCRTS - Command and Control Research and Technology Symposium

CINC - Commander in Chief

COBP - Code of Best Practice

CPOF - Command Post of the Future

CPX - Command Post Exercises

D

DARPA - Defense Advanced Research Projects Agency

DM - Dominant Maneuver

DoD - Department of Defense

DOTMLPF - Doctrine, Organization, Training, Material, Leadership, Personnel, and Facilities

DTIC - Defense Technical Information Center

E

EBO - Effects-Based Operations

ESC - Electronic Systems Center

ETO - Effects Tasking Orders

F

FTX - Field Training Exercise

G

GPS - Global Positioning System

H

HEAT - Headquarters Effectiveness Assessment Tool

HFS - Human Factors Society

HQ - Headquarters

I

ICCRTS - International Command and Control Research and Technology Symposium

IDEF-0 - a formal process modeling language, where activity boxes are named as verbs or verb phrases, and are connected via arrows, named as nouns or noun phrases, which define inputs (from the left), controls (from the top), outputs (to the right), or mechanisms (from the bottom). Each activity has a definition, keywords, and can be quantified by time, cost, frequency, etc.

IEEE - Institute of Electrical and Electronics Engineers

IQ - intelligence quotients

J

JEFX - Joint Expeditionary Force Exercise

JFCOM - Joint Forces Command

JROC - Joint Requirements Oversight Council

JTF - Joint Task Force

JV - Joint Vision

JWID - Joint Warrior Interoperability Demonstration

L

LOEs - Limited Objective Experiments

M

MCP - Mission Capability Packages

MOCE - Measures of C2 Effectiveness

MOFE - Measures of Force Effectiveness

MOP - Measures of Performance

MOPE - Measures of Policy Effectiveness

MORS - Military Operations Research Society

M&S - Modeling and Simulation

N

NATO - North Atlantic Treaty Organization

NCW - Network Centric Warfare

NGO - Non-Governmental Organization

O

ONA - Operational Net Assessments

OOB - Order of Battle

R

RDO - Rapid Decisive Operations

RPV - Remotely Piloted Vehicles

S

SME - Subject Matter Experts

STOW - Synthetic Theater of War

T

TD - Technology Demonstration

V

VIPs - Very Important Persons

VV&A - Verification, Validation & Accreditation

Bibliography

Alberts, David S., John J. Garstka, and Frederick P. Stein. *Network Centric Warfare: Developing and Leveraging Information Superiority.* Second Edition. Washington, DC: CCRP. 1999.

Alberts, David S. and Richard E. Hayes. *Command Arrangements for Peace Operations.* Washington, DC: NDU Press. 1995.

Alberts, David S. John J. Gartska, Richard E. Hayes, and David A. Signori. *Understanding Information Age Warfare.* Washington, DC: CCRP. 2001.

Bankes, Steve. "Exploratory Modeling for Policy Analysis." *Operations Research.* Linthicum, MD: INFORMS. 1993.

Bankes, Steve, Robert Lempert, and Steven Popper. "Computer-Assisted Reasoning." *CSE in Industry.* St Louis, MO: American Institute of Physics. 2001.

C4ISR Architecture Framework Version 2.0. Washington, DC: The Architecture Working Group and the Office of the Secretary of Defense. 1997.

DoD Instruction No. 5000.61. Subject: *DoD Modeling and Simulation (M&S) Verification, Validation, and Accreditation (VV&A).* October 5, 2001.

Headquarters Effectiveness Assessment Tool "HEAT" User's Manual. McLean, VA: Defense Systems, Inc. 1984.

Loerch, Andrew, Robert Koury, and Daniel Maxwell. *Value Added Analysis for Army Equipment Modernization.* New York, NY: John Wiley & Sons, Inc. 1999.

Ludwig Mies van der Rohe. *The New York Times.* August 19, 1969.

McBurney, D.H. *Research Methods.* Pacific Grove, CA: Brooks/Cole. 1994.

NATO COBP for Command and Control Assessment. Washington, DC: CCRP. 1998.

Network Centric Warfare Department of Defense Report to Congress. July 2001.

Schellenberger, Robert E. "Criteria for Assessing Model Validity for Managerial Purposes." *Decision Sciences Journal.* Atlanta, GA: Decision Sciences Institute. 1974. No. 5. pp644-653.

Vadum, Arlene and Neil Rankin. *Psychological Research Methods for Discovery and Validation.* Boston: McGraw Hill Higher Education. 1997.

About the Editors

Dr. Alberts is currently the Director, Research and Strategic Planning, OASD (C3I). Prior to this he was the Director, Advanced Concepts, Technologies, and Information Strategies (ACTIS), Deputy Director of the Institute for National Strategic Studies, and the executive agent for DoD's Command and Control Research Program. This included responsibility for the Center for Advanced Concepts and Technology (ACT) and the School of Information Warfare and Strategy (SIWS) at the National Defense University. He has more than 25 years of experience developing and introducing leading-edge technology into private and public sector organizations. This extensive applied experience is augmented by a distinguished academic career in computer science, operations research, and Government service in senior policy and management positions. Dr. Alberts' experience includes serving as a CEO for a high-technology firm specializing in the design and development of large, state-of-the-art computer systems (including expert, investigative, intelligence, information, and command and control systems) in both Government and industry. He has also led organizations engaged in research and analysis of command and control system performance and related contributions to operational missions. Dr. Alberts has had policy responsibility for corporate computer and telecommunications capabilities, facilities, and experimental laboratories. His responsibilities have also included management of research aimed at enhancing the usefulness of systems, extending their productive life, and the development of improved methods for evaluating the contributions that systems make to organizational functions. Dr. Alberts frequently contributes to Government task forces and workshops on systems acquisition, command and control, and systems evaluation.

As President and founder of Evidence Based Research, Inc., Dr. Hayes specializes in multidisciplinary analyses of command and control, intelligence, and national security issues; the identification of opportunities to improve support to decisionmakers in the defense and intelligence communities; the design and development of systems to provide that support; and the criticism, test, and evaluation of systems and procedures that provide such support. His areas of expertise include crisis management; political-military issues; research methods; experimental design; simulation and modeling; test and evaluation; military command, control, communication, and intelligence (C3I); and decision-aiding systems. Since coming to Washington in 1974, Dr. Hayes has established himself as a leader in bringing the systematic use of evidence and the knowledge base of the social sciences into play in support of decisionmakers in the national security community, domestic agencies, and major corporations. He has initiated several programs of research and lines of business that achieved national attention and many others that directly influenced policy development in client organizations.

Catalog of CCRP Publications

Coalition Command and Control*
(Maurer, 1994)

Peace operations differ in significant ways from traditional combat missions. As a result of these unique characteristics, command arrangements become far more complex. The stress on command and control arrangements and systems is further exacerbated by the mission's increased political sensitivity.

The Mesh and the Net
(Libicki, 1994)

Considers the continuous revolution in information technology as it can be applied to warfare in terms of capturing more information (mesh) and how people and their machines can be connected (net).

Command Arrangements for Peace Operations
(Alberts & Hayes, 1995)

By almost any measure, the U.S. experience shows that traditional C2 concepts, approaches, and doctrine are not particularly well suited for peace operations. This book (1) explores the reasons for this, (2) examines alternative command arrangement approaches, and (3) describes the attributes of effective command arrangements.

CCRP Publications

Standards: The Rough Road to the Common Byte
(Libicki, 1995)

The inability of computers to "talk" to one another is a major problem, especially for today's high technology military forces. This study by the Center for Advanced Command Concepts and Technology looks at the growing but confusing body of information technology standards. Among other problems, it discovers a persistent divergence between the perspectives of the commercial user and those of the government.

What Is Information Warfare?*
(Libicki, 1995)

Is Information Warfare a nascent, perhaps embryonic art, or simply the newest version of a time-honored feature of warfare? Is it a new form of conflict that owes its existence to the burgeoning global information infrastructure, or an old one whose origin lies in the wetware of the human brain but has been given new life by the Information Age? Is it a unified field or opportunistic assemblage?

Operations Other Than War*
(Alberts & Hayes, 1995)

This report documents the fourth in a series of workshops and roundtables organized by the INSS Center for Advanced Concepts and Technology (ACT). The workshop sought insights into the process of determining what technologies are required for OOTW. The group also examined the complexities of introducing relevant technologies and discussed general and specific OOTW technologies and devices.

Dominant Battlespace Knowledge*
(Johnson & Libicki, 1996)

The papers collected here address the most critical aspects of that problem—to wit: If the United States develops the means to acquire dominant battlespace knowledge, how might that affect the way it goes to war, the circumstances under which force can and will be used, the purposes for its employment, and the resulting alterations of the global geomilitary environment?

Interagency and Political-Military Dimensions of Peace Operations: Haiti - A Case Study
(Hayes & Wheatley, 1996)

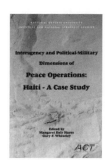

This report documents the fifth in a series of workshops and roundtables organized by the INSS Center for Advanced Concepts and Technology (ACT). Widely regarded as an operation that "went right," Haiti offered an opportunity to explore interagency relations in an operation close to home that had high visibility and a greater degree of interagency civilian-military coordination and planning than the other operations examined to date.

The Unintended Consequences of the Information Age*
(Alberts, 1996)

The purpose of this analysis is to identify a strategy for introducing and using Information Age technologies that accomplishes two things: first, the identification and avoidance of adverse unintended consequences associated with the introduction and utilization of information technologies; and second, the ability to recognize and capitalize on unexpected opportunities.

Joint Training for Information Managers*
(Maxwell, 1996)

This book proposes new ideas about joint training for information managers over Command, Control, Communications, Computers, and Intelligence (C4I) tactical and strategic levels. It suggests a substantially new way to approach the training of future communicators, grounding its argument in the realities of the fast-moving C4I technology.

Defensive Information Warfare*
(Alberts, 1996)

This overview of defensive information warfare is the result of an effort, undertaken at the request of the Deputy Secretary of Defense, to provide background material to participants in a series of interagency meetings to explore the nature of the problem and to identify areas of potential collaboration.

Command, Control, and the Common Defense
(Allard, 1996)

The author provides an unparalleled basis for assessing where we are and were we must go if we are to solve the joint and combined command and control challenges facing the U.S. military as it transitions into the 21st century.

CCRP Publications

Shock & Awe:
Achieving Rapid Dominance*
(Ullman & Wade, 1996)

The purpose of this book is to explore alternative concepts for structuring mission capability packages around which future U. S. military forces might be configured.

Information Age Anthology:
Volume I*
(Alberts & Papp, 1997)

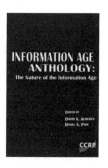

In this first volume, we will examine some of the broader issues of the Information Age: what the Information Age is; how it affects commerce, business, and service; what it means for the government and the military; and how it affects international actors and the international system.

Complexity, Global Politics,
and National Security*
(Alberts & Czerwinski, 1997)

The charge given by the President of the National Defense University and RAND leadership was three-fold: (1) push the envelope; (2) emphasize the policy and strategic dimensions of national defense with the implications for complexity theory; and (3) get the best talent available in academe.

CCRP Publications

Target Bosnia: Integrating Information Activities in Peace Operations*
(Siegel, 1998)

This book examines the place of PI and PSYOP in peace operations through the prism of NATO operations in Bosnia-Herzegovina.

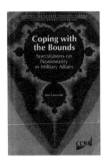

Coping with the Bounds
(Czerwinski, 1998)

The theme of this work is that conventional, or linear, analysis alone is not sufficient to cope with today's and tomorrow's problems, just as it was not capable of solving yesterday's. Its aim is to convince us to augment our efforts with nonlinear insights, and its hope is to provide a basic understanding of what that involves.

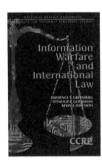

Information Warfare and International Law*
(Greenberg, Goodman, & Soo Hoo, 1998)

The authors, members of the Project on Information Technology and International Security at Stanford University's Center for International Security and Arms Control, have surfaced and explored some profound issues that will shape the legal context within which information warfare may be waged and national information power exerted in the coming years.

CCRP Publications

Lessons From Bosnia: The IFOR Experience*
(Wentz, 1998)

This book tells the story of the challenges faced and innovative actions taken by NATO and U.S. personnel to ensure that IFOR and Operation Joint Endeavor were military successes. A coherent C4ISR lessons learned story has been pieced together from firsthand experiences, interviews of key personnel, focused research, and analysis of lessons learned reports provided to the National Defense University team.

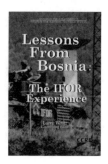

Doing Windows: Non-Traditional Military Responses to Complex Emergencies
(Hayes & Sands, 1999)

This book provides the final results of a project sponsored by the Joint Warfare Analysis Center. Our primary objective in this project was to examine how military operations can support the long-term objective of achieving civil stability and durable peace in states embroiled in complex emergencies.

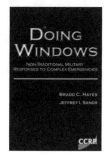

Network Centric Warfare
(Alberts, Garstka, & Stein, 1999)

It is hoped that this book will contribute to the preparations for NCW in two ways. First, by articulating the nature of the characteristics of Network Centric Warfare. Second, by suggesting a process for developing mission capability packages designed to transform NCW concepts into operational capabilities.

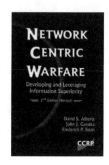

Behind the Wizard's Curtain
(Krygiel, 1999)

There is still much to do and more to learn and understand about developing and fielding an effective and durable infostructure as a foundation for the 21st century. Without successfully fielding systems of systems, we will not be able to implement emerging concepts in adaptive and agile command and control, nor will we reap the potential benefits of Network Centric Warfare.

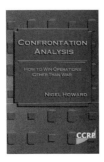

Confrontation Analysis:
How to Win Operations Other Than War
(Howard, 1999)

A peace operations campaign (or operation other than war) should be seen as a linked sequence of confrontations, in contrast to a traditional, warfighting campaign, which is a linked sequence of battles. The objective in each confrontation is to bring about certain "compliant" behavior on the part of other parties, until in the end the campaign objective is reached. This is a state of sufficient compliance to enable the military to leave the theater.

Information Campaigns
for Peace Operations
(Avruch, Narel, & Siegel, 2000)

In its broadest sense, this report asks whether the notion of struggles for control over information identifiable in situations of conflict also has relevance for situations of third-party conflict management—for peace operations.

Information Age Anthology:
Volume II*
(Alberts & Papp, 2000)

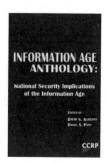

Is the Information Age bringing with it new challenges and threats, and if so, what are they? What sorts of dangers will these challenges and threats present? From where will they (and do they) come? Is information warfare a reality? This publication, Volume II of the Information Age Anthology, explores these questions and provides preliminary answers to some of them.

Information Age Anthology:
Volume III*
(Alberts & Papp, 2001)

In what ways will wars and the military that fight them be different in the Information Age than in earlier ages? What will this mean for the U.S. military? In this third volume of the Information Age Anthology, we turn finally to the task of exploring answers to these simply stated, but vexing questions that provided the impetus for the first two volumes of the Information Age Anthology.

Understanding Information Age Warfare
(Alberts, Garstka, Hayes, & Signori, 2001)

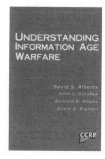

This book presents an alternative to the deterministic and linear strategies of the planning modernization that are now an artifact of the Industrial Age. The approach being advocated here begins with the premise that adaptation to the Information Age centers around the ability of an organization or an individual to utilize information.

Information Age Transformation
(Alberts, 2002)

This book is the first in a new series of CCRP books that will focus on the Information Age transformation of the Department of Defense. Accordingly, it deals with the issues associated with a very large governmental institution, a set of formidable impediments, both internal and external, and the nature of the changes being brought about by Information Age concepts and technologies.

Code of Best Practice for Experimentation
(CCRP, 2002)

Experimentation is the lynch pin in the DoD's strategy for transformation. Without a properly focused, well-balanced, rigorously designed, and expertly conducted program of experimentation, the DoD will not be able to take full advantage of the opportunities that Information Age concepts and technologies offer.

Lessons From Kosovo: The KFOR Experience
(Wentz, 2002)

Kosovo offered another unique opportunity for CCRP to conduct additional coalition C4ISR-focused research in the areas of coalition command and control, civil-military cooperation, information assurance, C4ISR interoperability, and information operations.

CCRP Publications

NATO Code of Best Practice for C2 Assessment
(2002)

To the extent that they can be achieved, significantly reduced levels of fog and friction offer an opportunity for the military to develop new concepts of operations, new organisational forms, and new approaches to command and control, as well as to the processes that support it. Analysts will be increasingly called upon to work in this new conceptual dimension in order to examine the impact of new information-related capabilities coupled with new ways of organising and operating.

Effects Based Operations
(Smith, 2003)

This third book of the Information Age Transformation Series speaks directly to what we are trying to accomplish on the "fields of battle" and argues for changes in the way we decide what effects we want to achieve and what means we will use to achieve them.

The Big Issue
(Potts, 2003)

This Occasional considers command and combat in the Information Age. It is an issue that takes us into the realms of the unknown. Defence thinkers everywhere are searching forward for the science and alchemy that will deliver operational success.

Power to the Edge: Command...Control... in the Information Age
(Alberts & Hayes, 2003)

Power to the Edge articulates the principles being used to provide the ubiquitous, secure, wideband network that people will trust and use, populate with high quality information, and use to develop shared awareness, collaborate effectively, and synchronize their actions.

Complexity Theory and Network Centric Warfare
(Moffat, 2003)

Professor Moffat articulates the mathematical models and equations that clearly demonstrate the relationship between warfare and the emergent behaviour of complex natural systems, as well as a means to calculate and assess the likely outcomes.

Campaigns of Experimentation: Pathways to Innovation and Transformation
(Alberts & Hayes, 2005)

In this follow-on to the Code of Best Practice for Experimentation, the concept of a campaign of experimentation is explored in detail. Key issues of discussion include planning, execution, achieving synergy, and avoiding common errors and pitfalls.

CCRP Publications

Somalia Operations: Lessons Learned (Allard, 2005)

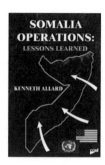

Originally published by NDU in 1995, this book is Colonel Allard's examination of the challenges and the successes of the U.S. peacekeeping mission to Somalia in 1992-1994. Key topics include planning, deployment, conduct of operations, and support.

The Agile Organization: From Informal Networks to Complex Effects and Agility (Atkinson & Moffat, 2005)

This book contains real-world observations, anecdotes, and historical vignettes that illustrate how organizations and networks function and how the connections between people, nature, societies, beliefs, the sciences, and the military can be understood in order to pursue the goal of an agile organization.